STO✓s

...rk
POCAHONTAS, *Seym...*
PONTIAC, *Peckham...*
SACAGAWEA, *Seymo...*
SEQUOYAH, *Snow...*
SITTING BULL, *Stev...*
SQUANTO, *Stevenson...*
TECUMSEH, *Stevenso...*

NAVAL HE...ES

DAVID FARRAGUT, *...*
GEORGE DEWEY, *L...*
JOHN PAUL JONES, *...*
MATTHEW CALBRAI... ...RRY, *Scharbach*
OLIVER HAZARD P... *Long*
RAPHAEL SEMMES, *...*
STEPHEN DECATUR, *...*

NOTED WI...S
and MOTHE...S

ABIGAIL ADAMS, *W...*
DOLLY MADISON, *M...*
ELEANOR ROOSEVEL... *...*
JESSIE FREMONT, *W...*
MARTHA WASHING... *...agoner*
MARY TODD LINC... *...ilkie*
NANCY HANKS, *Ste...son*
RACHEL JACKSON, *Covan*

SCIENTISTS
and
INVENTORS

ABNER DOUBLEDAY, *Dunham*
ALBERT EINSTEIN, *Hammontree*
ALECK BELL, *Widdemer*
CYRUS MCCORMICK, *Dobler*
ELI WHITNEY, *Snow*
ELIAS HOWE, *Corcoran*
ELIZABETH BLACKWELL, *Henry*
GAIL BORDEN, *Paradis*
GEORGE CARVER, *Stevenson*
GEORGE EASTMAN, *Henry*
GEORGE PULLMAN, *Myers*
GEORGE WESTINGHOUSE, *Dunham*
HENRY FORD, *Aird and Ruddiman*
JOHN AUDUBON, *Mason*
JOHN BURROUGHS, *Frisbee*
JOHN DEERE, *Bare*
LEE DEFOREST, *Dobler*
LUTHER BURBANK, *Burt*
MARIA MITCHELL, *Melin*
ROBERT FULTON, *Henry*
SAMUEL MORSE, *Snow*
TOM EDISON, *Guthridge*
WALTER REED, *Higgins*

LEADERS

BETSY ROSS, *Weil*
BOOKER T. WASHINGTON, *Stevenson*
CLARA BARTON, *Stevenson*
DAN BEARD, *Mason*
DOROTHEA DIX, *Melin*
FRANCES WILLARD, *Mason*
J. STERLING MORTON, *Moore*
JANE ADDAMS, *Wagoner*
JULIA WARD HOWE, *Wagoner*
JULIETTE LOW, *Higgins*
LILIUOKALANI, *Newman*
LUCRETIA MOTT, *Burnett*
MOLLY PITCHER, *Stevenson*
OLIVER WENDELL HOLMES, JR., *Dunham*
SUSAN ANTHONY, *Monsell*

SOLDIERS

ANTHONY WAYNE, *Stevenson*
BEDFORD FORREST, *Parks*
DAN MORGAN, *Bryant*
DOUGLAS MACARTHUR, *Long*
ETHAN ALLEN, *Winders*
FRANCIS MARION, *Steele*
GEORGE CUSTER, *Stevenson*

STATESMEN

ABE LINCOLN, *Stevenson*
ANDY JACKSON, *Stevenson*
DAN WEBSTER, *Smith*
FRANKLIN ROOSEVELT, *Weil*
HENRY CLAY, *Monsell*
HERBERT HOOVER, *Comfort*
JAMES MONROE, *Widdemer*
JEFF DAVIS, *de Grummond and Delaune*
JOHN F. KENNEDY, *Frisbee*
JOHN MARSHALL, *Monsell*
TEDDY ROOSEVELT, *Parks*
WOODROW WILSON, *Monsell*

Andrew Carnegie

Young Steelmaker

Illustrated by George Armstrong

Andrew Carnegie

Young Steelmaker

By Joanne Landers Henry

 THE **BOBBS-MERRILL** COMPANY, INC.
A SUBSIDIARY OF HOWARD W. SAMS & CO., INC.
Publishers · INDIANAPOLIS · NEW YORK

LIBRARY OF CONGRESS CATALOG CARD NUMBER: 66-18415

PRINTED IN THE UNITED STATES OF AMERICA

To the memory of D. L. C.

Illustrations

Contents

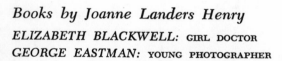

Books by Joanne Landers Henry

ELIZABETH BLACKWELL: GIRL DOCTOR

GEORGE EASTMAN: YOUNG PHOTOGRAPHER

★ Andrew Carnegie

Young Steelmaker

"There's the Bookman!"

Six - year - old Andy whistled happily as he walked beside his father. He pushed his tousled blond hair from his eyes and hurried to keep pace with Mr. Carnegie. Andy felt especially happy today. This was the first time his father had allowed him to go to the village cotton mill.

"You're the best weaver in all Dunfermline, Father!" Andy said proudly. He took a tighter grip on his father's black top hat. The hat was filled with bobbins, or spools, of new yarn. Mr. Carnegie would weave this new yarn into tablecloths and napkins.

Andy's father laughed. "You're a boastful lad.

Our small village is filled with weavers—the most skilled in all Scotland, some say." Mr. Carnegie slowed his pace and looked down at his short, stout-legged son.

Early that spring morning Andy and his father had walked to the cotton mill. They had carried with them fine white table linens. These had been woven on the large hand looms in Mr. Carnegie's shop.

Andy had listened proudly while the man at the mill had praised his father's work. The table linens would sell for a good price, the man had said. Then he had given Mr. Carnegie several spools of new yarn to use in making more table linens.

Now Andy and his father were on their way home. They lived in a modest gray stone cottage at the foot of Edgar Street.

Andy scuffed the brown cobblestones of the street with one shoe. Then he looked up thoughtfully at his father. "May I go to the mill with you the next time you go, Father?"

Mr. Carnegie smiled broadly. "We'll see, Andy, but now we must make haste home to the shop. The three men at the shop will be waiting for the spools of new yarn. Who knows what has happened while we've been gone?"

They passed along busy High Street, which was the center of the village. From High Street, they turned onto a much narrower street which sloped gently downhill. The village was nestled on the side of a great rolling hill that looked toward the city of Edinburgh.

A peddler with a bundle of thin twigs on his back passed them. "Spunk, spunk — kindling wood for sale!" he called.

The spring sun was shining brightly, but the narrow streets were shaded. The gray stone houses which were crowded close together shut off the sunlight from the street.

Andy hurried ahead of his father as they turned down Priory Lane. They turned a corner again and then another. Andy skipped past the cottages of the other weavers, who were their neighbors. Now he could see at the very end of the street the two-storied cottage that was his home. Beyond it lay Reid's Park.

The ground floor of the cottage was his father's shop. There, in a single large room, stood four looms. The Carnegies lived on the second floor, above the shop.

Suddenly Andy stopped and pointed. "Father! Father!" He waved toward a man who was just coming out of the shop's door. The man carried a heavy pack on his shoulders. He wore a black top hat and shiny black boots.

Mr. Carnegie quickened his step. "Aye, Andy! There's the bookman! We seem to have arrived home just in time. A few more minutes and we would have missed him."

14

Andy grinned. The bookman went from village to village and from house to house, selling books. Book stores were found only in large cities like Edinburgh. What would people have to enjoy, Andy wondered, if it weren't for books. He couldn't imagine a world without books.

Andy thought of the pleasure the new books would bring. Every evening after supper his father would read aloud. Andy would sit near his father's feet and listen. Sometimes his father would read the same book two or three times, especially if it was one of his favorites. Andy didn't mind hearing a book read over and over. He loved the sounds of words, even though he didn't know what all the words meant.

Close behind the bookman, Mrs. Carnegie appeared in the doorway. With an excited shout Andy waved to his mother. He clutched the top hat beneath one arm and darted on as fast as his legs would carry him.

Suddenly his foot struck against one of the uneven cobblestones and he stumbled forward with a cry. The top hat, filled with spools of shining new yarn, flew out of his grasp. He fell flat on the stones.

Mrs. Carnegie gathered up her long skirts and rushed to his side. "Andy! Are you hurt?"

16

Andy's face flushed red as he got to his feet. His nose was skinned and his hands and knees were covered with dust. Large tears came to his eyes, but he held them back.

"No, Mother," he answered with a stubborn shake of his head. "I'm not hurt, but I've spilled Father's spools. Now I won't get to go to the mill to carry spools home again." He looked up into his father's stern face.

With a quick laugh, the bookman put his pack down on the street. Within a few seconds he had gathered up the spools and put them back in the hat.

"There's scarcely a trace of dust on them," he said, smiling. With a bow, he handed the hat to Andy. "The moral of this story is, laddie: proceed with care if you wish to get ahead—instead of down—in this world."

At the bookman's words, Mr. Carnegie's look softened. He turned to the man. "As you say,

Duncan, there's little harm done. I'll not punish the lad. Perhaps this will teach him not to try to get ahead so fast." He winked at the bookman and Mrs. Carnegie.

Mrs. Carnegie smoothed her skirts. With a smile she urged the bookman and her husband inside the shop. "I'll make some tea while Mr. Carnegie looks over your new books, Mr. Duncan," she said cheerfully.

"May I look, too?" Andy put in quickly. "I can clean the spools while I watch."

"He's a spunky lad, Carnegie—full of fire," said Mr. Duncan. "And a bargainer, too!"

Mr. Carnegie nodded as he followed Mrs. Carnegie and the bookman inside. He motioned Andy to join them as they passed through the door. Andy's blue eyes sparkled as he followed the grown-ups into the shop.

The three weavers who worked for Mr. Carnegie turned and nodded a greeting. They kept

18

their looms busy, however, and did not stop to talk. *Clack, clack, clack* went the looms as the shuttles sped back and forth.

A kettle of boiling water hung over the fire in the fireplace. Soon the tea was made and Mrs. Carnegie started to work. She began to wind the pirns, or small spools of thread, which were used in the shuttles.

Mr. Carnegie went through the books in Mr. Duncan's pack one by one. He said Andy could look at the books as he finished with them. With great care, Andy touched the books. Most of them were cheap editions with heavy paper covers. A few of the books were bound in fine leather and had gold printing on their covers. Andy marveled at how handsome these books were. They were too expensive for his father to consider buying.

At last Mr. Carnegie selected three books and paid for them. One was the latest installment of a novel by Charles Dickens. It was *The Old Curiosity Shop.* The stories by Mr. Dickens were among Andy's favorites.

Andy dusted the spools of new thread on his sleeve and listened as the men talked. His father seemed worried by the news Mr. Duncan brought. The weavers throughout Scotland said that steam power soon would replace hand looms. Then the weavers would have no work.

"Aye, we've heard much talk like this in our village," agreed Mr. Carnegie. "My linens still bring a good price, but this is 1842. In a few years I fear we'll be poorer."

Andy could not remain quiet any longer. "Father, do you mean the looms here will be run by steam engines?"

His father glanced at him. "Yes, Andy, that's right. The looms will be run by steam engines —by machinery—instead of men, people say."

That evening after supper the family gathered

by the fireside. Mr. Carnegie opened the new novel by Charles Dickens. Andy was eager to hear his father read, but he kept thinking about his accident with the spools. He feared that his father wouldn't let him go again to the mill.

"Father," he said, "I want more work to do. I can do more than clear the table and sweep the shop floor. Would you let me show you, so that I can go to the mill again?"

"Well, lad, you're only six. I'll have a talk with your mother. Perhaps we can find work your size," Mr. Carnegie added with a wink.

Mrs. Carnegie nodded. "Yes, Andy, tomorrow morning we'll see. It won't be anything grand, but I'm sure you'll be able to help."

Andy's eyes glistened. Tomorrow, he was sure, would be a very special day.

"You Are in Trouble, Andy!"

ANDY was awake early the next morning. He could scarcely see out the window because a low fog hung over the ground. It almost hid his mother's small vegetable garden in the back yard. Each house on the street had a tiny garden, where the housewife raised as many vegetables as she could for her family.

Eagerly Andy jumped out of bed. The chill morning air made him shiver. He dressed as quickly as he could while his mother worked near the glowing fire in the fireplace. She was busy stirring a large pot of oatmeal porridge for the family's breakfast.

"Good morning, Andy," she called cheerfully. "Run along and wash. Your father is outside washing at the rain barrel. Hurry because breakfast is nearly ready."

Andy was eager to know about the new work he was to do today. He knew, however, that he must wait for his parents to tell him.

Soon the family was seated at the polished wood table near the fire. Andy was hungry and the steaming hot oatmeal smelled very good to him. This morning his mother had a special treat for him. She gave him some coarse brown sugar to use on his cereal!

Mr. Carnegie broke off a large chunk of bread and passed it to Andy. "Here, lad, eat hearty. You've a job to do this morning."

"Oh, Father!" cried Andy. "Please tell me what it is. I can't wait any longer!"

Mrs. Carnegie smiled gently as Mr. Carnegie spoke. "As you know, Andy, every day your mother carries our drinking water from the village well. There is no well here at home."

"I know, Father," Andy said. "All the villagers use a common well."

"It takes a lot of strength to lug two heavy pails of water. Do you think you are strong enough, Andy?" asked Mrs. Carnegie.

"Oh, yes, I'm sure I am, Mother," said Andy. "And I know my way—I won't get lost."

"Good!" said Mr. Carnegie. "I can't leave the shop every day to go to the well, and your mother has much work to do here at home. We must have fresh drinking water. So it's a responsible job I'm giving you."

Andy smiled with pride. "Wait until my cousin Dod hears about my job of carrying water," he thought. He considered Dod his best friend and managed to play with him almost every day. Dod's father ran a greengrocery, or grocery store in Scotland.

As soon as breakfast was over, Mr. Carnegie went down to his shop. Andy could hear the muffled *clack, clack, clack* of the busy looms as he helped his mother clear the table. At last his tasks were done, and he set off for the village well. Happily he climbed the gentle hill to the top of Edgar Street.

It seemed to Andy that no matter where he went he was walking uphill or down. From the hillside, he could see the gently rolling Pentland Hills to the south. Beyond these beautiful hills he could see the sparkling blue sea waters of the Firth of Forth, a long narrow arm of the sea. He thought that it looked like a lake. On brilliantly clear days he could make out the church spires of the great city of Edinburgh on the other side of the water.

As Andy walked on toward the well, he passed a next-door neighbor, Ailie Fargie. She was one of his mother's best friends.

"Good morning!" Andy called cheerfully.

Ailie Fargie smiled a greeting as she busily finished sweeping the front step of her cottage. Many of the other housewives were busy sweeping their front steps, too. Andy called out to each as he passed by their cottages.

Some of the wives were going where Andy was going—to the village well. One old woman, who walked ahead of him, was carrying a large pitcher. A young housewife, wearing a long dress with a shawl thrown over her shoulders, carried a large bucket.

At last Andy came to the well. "As soon as I hurry home with the water," he thought, "I'll find Dod. Won't he be surprised when he hears I've carried water from the well!"

Suddenly Andy stopped and looked with surprise toward the well. There was a long line of women and boys waiting their turn to draw water. Slowly the line moved forward.

26

" 'Tis a bother to have the well run so slow," one woman complained to another. "I need water the first thing in the morning, but there's always a line here early."

"We pay a high price in lost time—to stand and wait," said another woman with a shake of her head. "I haven't the time after supper to bring my pitcher here as some do."

"Aye!" answered the first woman with a laugh. "Some leave their pitchers and pails here all night. The waiting in the morning is shorter than during the day."

Impatiently Andy stood on one foot, then the other at the end of the line. At this rate, he'd miss going to Dod's before noon.

"I won't wait longer," he said to himself with a frown. Then, without thinking, he raced to the head of the line.

A boy somewhat larger than Andy reached out for the empty well bucket, but Andy was faster

than the older boy. He grabbed the bucket and lowered it with a splash into the well and commenced to haul it out again.

"Here!" cried the boy. "It's not your turn to get water."

Andy hung onto the bucket's ropes, determined to get his share of the water first. He worked quickly, taking advantage of the other boy's surprise at his action.

"I'm in a hurry," shouted Andy, "and I won't wait longer." He held the filled bucket and threatened to douse the larger boy.

Quickly the boy backed away and Andy filled his smaller pails. By now the housewives were clacking their tongues and scolding Andy for his bad manners.

Andy's cheeks turned red with embarrassment. Now he realized that the women were right, but he hadn't meant to be rude. He had just wanted to get water as fast as possible. He grabbed his filled pails and started toward home without looking at the women again. Next time he would wait his turn, he decided.

The bigger boy shook his fist at Andy's back. "I'll get even with you," he shouted angrily, "and this is your warning."

Andy pretended not to hear the boy. He felt guilty, but the boy's threat made him angry. "If I ever have to fight this boy," he said, "I'll be fair. And I'll beat him, for being so revengeful and selfish."

Soon Andy's arms began to ache from carrying the heavy pails. Before he reached the foot of Edgar Street, he stopped to rest.

"Should I tell Mother what happened at the well?" he wondered while he was waiting. Soon he picked up the heavy pails again and started on his way. Perhaps his father would punish him, or not let him go to the well again. What was the right thing for him to do?

At last Andy reached his cottage. He carried the water pails up the stone staircase to the family's room over the shop. The staircase was on the outside of the cottage, and was protected by an iron hand-rail.

"Why, the pails are very nearly full!" said his mother. "You've managed nicely."

Andy thought of what had happened at the well. Somehow his mother's words made him feel uncomfortable because he had obtained the water out of turn. He tried to tell her what had happened, but couldn't find the right words.

"I'll go to see Dod," he decided. "At least maybe I can tell Dod about it."

Andy asked his mother whether he might go to his uncle's greengrocery store and she readily consented. Then off he raced to the store. With a shout, he flung open the door and the bell above the door tinkled gaily.

"Why, hello, Andy!" Uncle Lauder gave him

a warm welcome. He came from behind the counter to greet Andy. He was tall and slender, unlike Andy's father, and his shoulders were slightly stooped. His gray eyes twinkled as he looked down at Andy.

"Since there's no school today, I suppose you've come to find Dod, eh?"

"That's right, Uncle Lauder," replied Andy, looking at the good things to eat. There were always sweets to be had, and sacks and barrels to look into. There were barrels of fish—whiting and herring—and stacked near the rough wooden counter were sacks of onions and potatoes. On the shelves were sugar, salt, flour, and tea. And sometimes there were fresh fruits and vegetables in the shop, too.

"Dod, Dod!" Uncle Lauder called toward the back room. "You have a visitor."

Dod came running into the shop. "Good-day to you, Andy!" he cried happily. He carried a large book under one arm. His hair was silken and brown like his father's and hung down over one eye.

"You boys run along outside and play," Uncle Lauder urged with a smile. "It's a fine spring day, and your school work can wait till this evening, Dod."

"I'm glad I don't go to school," Andy put in. "I can go out every day. I'd hate to sit in a stuffy old schoolroom all the time."

Uncle Lauder's eyes twinkled as he shook his finger at the boy. "Young lad, you are missing one of the best things in life—an education. You'll not go far unless you learn to read and write and do sums."

Andy looked down and scuffed one shoe on the floor. "Father has taught me to read a few words. Maybe someday I'll go to school—just to learn to read."

Andy's parents had promised him that he

33

didn't have to go to school until he was eight. They said that if he didn't want to learn, his schooling would be wasted. Some of the neighbors criticized Mr. Carnegie for keeping Andy at home, but he stood firm.

"Come on, Andy," Dod called from the doorway. "We haven't much time before dinner."

The boys headed for the palace ruins near Pittencrieff Glen, one of their favorite places to play. The glen, or narrow valley, was not far from High Street. Its grassy meadows, dotted with gnarled old trees, seemed wild and lonely. Somehow Andy always found adventure here. The sight of the ruins of the ancient palace wall with the great Abbey or church behind them stirred his imagination.

Dod was a little older and bigger than Andy, and a good runner. It took all the strength Andy had to keep up with him. Andy's feet pounded the cobblestones. He clenched his fists and held his head high. He made a last effort to overtake Dod before they reached the glen. Slowly he caught up and went around him.

With a shout and a laugh Andy reached the towering gray stones of the palace wall first. He rolled down in the high grass to rest. Laughing, Dod rolled down in the grass, too.

"Whew, Andy! That was a hard race!"

"Aye," Andy agreed. "You're a good runner, but I beat you."

After the boys had caught their breath, Andy sat up and began to talk. "I've a piece of news for you. I have an enemy."

Surprised, Dod jerked himself up. He listened as Andy told him about his trip to the well and how he had made the boy angry.

"I tried to tell Mother that I did wrong, but I couldn't explain," Andy added. "Now I'm afraid Father won't let me go to the well again. I'll probably be punished."

Dod shook his head. "You got yourself into trouble for sure this morning, Andy."

"I guess I did," replied Andy. "I didn't think of the wrong I was doing. I was in such a hurry, I took the quickest way."

For a few minutes the boys sat in silence. At last Andy said, "I'll tell my parents tonight after supper. Then I'll take my punishment, whatever it happens to be."

Slowly Dod got to his feet. "Tell me about the boy who is angry at you. What does he look like? Maybe I know him."

Andy started to describe the other boy. "That must be Malcolm McCain!" interrupted Dod. "He's one of the toughest boys in school. He's well liked but hard to beat in a fight. I'm afraid that you're really in trouble. If Malcolm said that he'd get you, he will."

"I'm not afraid," Andy said, jumping to his feet. "I'm a hard fighter, too."

"Well, if I were you, I'd be afraid," said Dod, glancing up at the sun. It was high overhead now. "I've got to get home for dinner. I'll meet you here later today. In the meantime watch out for Malcolm. This is one fight you're sure to lose." Then waving his hand, Dod turned to leave for home.

"I'll watch out for Malcolm, but I'm not afraid," said Andy. "After dinner I'll come back here to meet you and play with you."

Andy Learns a Lesson

IT WAS midafternoon before Andy could leave the cottage. He still was disturbed about his trouble with Malcolm, but really didn't expect anything to happen for a while.

Quickly he set off up the hill, eager again to explore the palace ruins. When he reached the palace, he looked up at one of the high empty windows in the great wall. Perhaps the great Scottish king Robert the Bruce had once looked out of this very window. The palace had been the home of a number of Scottish kings, for Dunfermline formerly had been the ancient capital of Scotland.

38

As Andy came near the wall, he looked one way and then another, hoping to see Dod, but could find no sign of him. Suddenly he heard a rustle from the thick brush behind him and called, "Dod, come out."

The brush parted, and the look of pleasure on Andy's face disappeared. There in front of him stood Malcolm, apparently ready to fight. Behind Malcolm was a great dark hole that marked the beginning of one of the palace's old underground passageways.

Malcolm peered at Andy with a cold angry look. "So you've come," he said.

Andy scowled back and squared his shoulders. "Aye, I've come!" he said. "So what?" With a sharp look he carefully studied his opponent. Malcolm weighed at least ten pounds more than he and was a good half head taller.

Despite his bold words, Andy felt a little scared. Perhaps, as Dod said, he was no match for the older boy. Malcolm might indeed give him a proper licking.

"I told you that I'd teach you a lesson, but I hate to give a small boy a beating. This time I'll not——"

"I'll show you that I'm not so small, Malcolm McCain!" Andy said hotly. He peeled off his jacket and put up his fists. No one was going to call him small!

Malcolm shrugged, threw his jacket to the ground, and faced Andy with raised fists. Andy rushed forward and struck at Malcolm as hard as he could. Malcolm dodged quickly and landed a blow on Andy's right shoulder.

Andy winced with pain, but was determined to put up a good fight. He sprang forward, grabbed Malcolm, and tried to throw him to the ground, but Malcolm threw him to the ground instead. The first thing he knew Malcolm sat astride him, holding his arms at his sides.

Malcolm grinned down at Andy. "Shall we call it a draw? You're a plucky lad—I under-estimated your strength."

Andy thought of Dod's words and remem-bered that Malcolm was well liked. His feeling of hatred toward Malcolm disappeared. After all he himself had started the trouble.

Malcolm got up and reached out his hand to help Andy. Then Andy got up and said, "You won the fight fairly, Malcolm. If you want to call the fight a draw, it surely will be a good bar-gain for me."

Malcolm threw back his head and laughed. Andy joined him. Soon the two boys were talk-ing like old friends.

"Next time I meet a fellow bigger than me," Andy said with a laugh, "I'll fight with my head instead of my fists. It's harder and likely to do more damage."

Malcolm gave another laugh, then urged

Andy to come with him. "I'm going to look for more secret passages in the palace."

Andy was happy to go along. "We'll keep an eye out for Dod," he said.

The boys climbed over the great heavy stones and through the tall grass. They searched for a new entryway into the passages and Malcolm told Andy of the many kings and princes who were buried nearby in the Abbey.

"More kings are buried here in our village than in any other place in Scotland," he said with pride.

Andy had heard many of these stories before, but he marveled at Malcolm's knowledge of Scottish history. Malcolm said he had learned his history at school.

Malcolm's pride in Scotland's history stirred Andy's imagination anew, and he soon found himself asking question after question. He was eager to know more. Perhaps, he thought, going to school wouldn't be such a bad thing after all. Malcolm seemed to enjoy it.

That evening after supper the Carnegie family gathered around the glowing embers of the fire. The dishes had been cleaned and neatly stacked in the corner cupboard. Mr. Carnegie sat, relaxed, in his chair near the hearth. Mrs. Carnegie sat, darning some of Andy's socks.

Andy had not forgotten his decision to tell them what had happened. "Father, Mother," he began, "I must tell you what happened today. It's something I have to tell you."

Both Mr. and Mrs. Carnegie nodded approval, and Andy began to tell his story. He told how he had made people angry at the well. Then he told about his fight with Malcolm, and how he had been beaten.

"I—I'm sorry for what I did," he concluded, "and now I'll think before I act."

Mr. Carnegie gave Andy a stern look. "Aye,

Andy. It was rude for you to act as you did this morning. I should punish you."

Andy knew that his father was right and waited for his mother to speak. Mrs. Carnegie raised her eyes from her work, and said, "A job isn't well done unless it's done right. Experience is a good teacher. Perhaps you learned your lesson today from Malcolm."

Andy sat, his hands folded tight in his lap. He felt ashamed and had to bite his lip to hold the tears back.

Mr. Carnegie stared down at his son. He leaned forward and looked into Andy's eyes. "Today you were beaten in a fight and that's hard for a Scottish lad to take. Malcolm punished you enough. We'll give you another chance."

"Oh, thank you, Father!" Andy cried. "I promise not to forget what you have said."

Andy felt so happy he rushed on to tell his

parents more about Malcolm. He told them about the school which Malcolm attended, and added, "Maybe someday soon I'd like to go there. Malcolm knows history and told me many interesting things about old Scottish kings. Besides he is a good fighter!" Andy finished admiringly.

Andy's parents exchanged smiles. They felt that possibly this had been a good day for Andy after all. He was learning and growing.

"Maybe you've learned many good things today to remember in later life, Andy," said his father, with a wink at Mrs. Carnegie.

A Strange Noise
Wakens Andy

THE FOLLOWING summer days passed quickly in the village. Andy was happy and busy but he could tell that something was worrying his parents. He wondered what it was.

One day trouble broke out in the village. Weavers and other workers left their shops and hurried angrily through the streets. When Andy's father heard what was happening, he ordered Andy to stay home. The weavers and miners of the village might riot, he said. They threatened to damage the factories and offices of certain unpopular employers.

Within the past few days there had been a few

small riots near Dunfermline. The workers complained that they were growing poorer while the government and people in high places were growing richer.

The workers blamed the voting laws and the corn laws for their troubles. The voting laws allowed only landowners or persons who paid high rent to vote. The corn laws made the price of grain so high that poor people couldn't afford to purchase flour for their families.

Mr. Carnegie watched the workers roaming about the streets. He was determined to take no part in the rioting.

"For the most part the people are right," he explained to Andy. "It's unfair that only people who own property or pay high rent can vote, and the corn laws are making our country poor. The change, however, should come through reform —a change in the laws—not through violence."

"Can you vote, Father?" asked Andy.

"No, I can't, lad, but I've spoken out many times in favor of reform, just as your Uncle Tom Morrison has. He has a great following among the people of the village, and in all the land around Dunfermline."

Mr. Carnegie shook his head. "This will be a sad day for him, too. He feels that rioting and fighting are wrong."

By nightfall Andy could still hear angry shouting in the streets. After dark he looked out the window and saw a red glow in the distance. "What is that, Father?" he cried.

Mr. Carnegie sadly shook his head and said, "The rioters have set fire to a factory. We only hope and pray that the damage which they cause will not ruin everybody—factory owners and workers alike."

Suddenly there was a loud knock at the door. Mr. Carnegie answered and there stood Tom Morrison. He looked tired and worried.

"Welcome, Tom," Mr. Carnegie said. "Come in and rest. We're anxious to hear the news."

Quickly and quietly Mrs. Carnegie set to work. "Yes, Tom, make yourself comfortable. I'll fix you a steaming cup of tea."

Andy admired his uncle, but he did not feel he knew him as well as Uncle Lauder. Uncle Tom was a large, impressive-looking man, lank and dark-haired. He and Andy's father spent long hours talking politics. He was one of the leaders of the village who had worked hard to persuade the government to give the people more liberty.

"The news I bring tonight is shocking," Uncle Tom said. "The rioters are setting out to burn factories, smash shop windows, and stone some of the shopkeepers and factory owners. This rioting must be stopped!"

Andy sat quietly by the fireplace and listened as the grown-ups talked. He felt frightened by their words. It seemed terrible to have the peace of the village shattered.

As Andy continued to listen, he was greatly shocked at his uncle's words. "Within a few days, I've been told, the troops will be here," his uncle went on to say. "They'll put a stop to the riots—with guns and bloodshed. Something must be done to stop the workers before then. I have determined to try to stop all this rioting tomorrow."

"But how?" asked Mrs. Carnegie. "What can you do to stop them?"

"I have a plan to put to them and have called a meeting tomorrow at Abbey Pends," replied Uncle Tom wearily. "Today I tried to stop them, but only got pushed around for my efforts. Perhaps by tomorrow their tempers will have cooled and they will listen to reason."

The following day news of the meeting spread through the village. The angry workers came to hear Tom Morrison speak. He told them not to riot again. He said they could show their anger in a peaceful way — through a general strike. The workers listened and were stirred by his words. At the end of the meeting, they shouted and applauded his plan.

Mr. Carnegie sighed with relief after the meeting was over. "I feared the government would try to stop the strike by coming to arrest Uncle Tom," he told Andy. "He has called a meeting in the nearby village of Torryburn for tomorrow night. If those workers agree to strike, the government troops won't have anyone to fight in our district."

That night the members of the Carnegie family went to bed with lighter and happier hearts. Andy had scarcely fallen asleep, however, when a strange noise suddenly wakened him. It sounded like the sharp clatter of stones against the window. Then the noise was repeated.

Andy ran to the window and threw it open.
The rough wood floor felt cold to his bare feet.
He leaned over the sill, looked down, and saw
two men standing in the dark shadows.

"Lad!" one of the men called. "Tell your father that Tom Morrison has been arrested. We're on our way to help him." Then before Andy could reply, the men disappeared.

"Father!" Andy turned and called. "Wake up—wake up! Uncle Tom has been arrested."

Mr. Carnegie hastily jumped out of bed and put on his clothes. "Evidently something has happened," he said. "I must hurry to see whether there's anything I can do to help Tom."

"Please let me go with you, Father!" Andy pleaded. "Please let me go." He was so determined that Mr. Carnegie hesitated.

"I think it will be safe for you to come," he said. "The fighting is over."

Andy's mother nodded slowly. "Yes, if Andy's old enough to think of school, he's old enough to go with his father."

Andy grinned with pride. Quickly he dressed and joined his father.

Mr. Carnegie and Andy went along the dark streets to High Street. A large crowd had collected to protest Tom Morrison's arrest. Some of the men carried flaming torches which cast shadows on the windows along the street. There were angry murmurings as the men pushed forward to the two-story stone building where the sheriff was holding Tom Morrison prisoner.

Suddenly Andy jerked his father's sleeve. "Look, there's Uncle Tom." He pointed to a window on the second floor.

Uncle Tom stood facing the crowd from the open window. He held up his hands and motioned the men to be silent. There were shouts of "Turn him loose! Turn him loose! He hasn't done anything to deserve punishment."

At last Uncle Tom succeeded in quieting the crowd. The angry murmuring ceased. Each man strained to hear Uncle Tom's words. His strong voice sounded out through the streets.

"How many of you here tonight are my friends?" he asked. "Show your hands!"

There was a great shout from the crowd. Andy stood on tiptoe. It was difficult for him to see what was going on. Cautiously he climbed on a fence to see better. He noticed that all other hands were raised and put both of his hands into the air.

Uncle Tom spoke again. "Then, my friends, if you want to help me, go home in peace. And keep the peace." With a friendly wave, he turned and disappeared inside the building.

Gradually the clusters of men in the street scattered toward their homes. With Andy by his side, Mr. Carnegie made his way toward the sheriff's office. Before he reached the door he was stopped by a friend. The man told him that Uncle Tom would be released temporarily.

With a smile the man added, "The sheriff has gone too far this time. He has no just cause for arresting Tom. He won't be able to stop the strike this way. He's made a bad mistake. Mark my words—Tom won't go to trial."

Mr. Carnegie thanked the man for the news. Then, with a look of great relief on his face, he turned to speak to Andy. "Well, lad, you've seen a bit of history in the making tonight. Your uncle will be on his way home soon. And that's where we should be heading. And your mother will scold us for staying out so late!" he added jokingly.

With a grin, Andy took his father's hand and walked home through the quiet, dark streets. Perhaps, he thought to himself, Uncle Tom would one day win his fight for greater liberty in Scotland. He certainly knew how to fight with words and was able to win.

The Ghost in the Graveyard

SEVEN-YEAR-OLD Andy liked to work with his mother in the tiny garden at the rear of their cottage. Spring had come and he liked to watch the flowers. The tulips were beginning to bloom. The sweet peas were growing taller by the day and the dahlia shoots were showing above the loose soil.

With a small wooden hand spade, Andy carefully dug and loosened the soil. Then he sorted out the weeds from the soil and threw them in a pile at one side.

Just then a tall thin man came round the side of the cottage into the garden. He wore a long black coat that came down to his knees and a high white collar with a neat black bow tie. He tipped his tall black top hat in friendly greeting to Mrs. Carnegie.

"Good day to you, Mrs. Carnegie," he said calmly. The man's speech sounded abrupt, yet somehow he struck Andy as being a rather friendly person. "I'm Dominie Martin."

"You are welcome, Dominie," said Mrs. Carnegie. "I am glad you have come."

Andy knew at once that the dominie was the teacher in Dod's school, but what did the dominie want here? Possibly if he listened closely, he would find out.

"This is our son, Andrew, who is helping me," said Mrs. Carnegie.

"He's a sturdy-looking lad and a very good worker," said Mr. Martin, nodding in Andy's direction. "I've been talking with his father and have come here to ask him à question."

Andy looked puzzled. What question could the dominie want to ask him? He had never even seen the dominie before.

The schoolmaster glanced at Mrs. Carnegie, but spoke directly to Andy. "I plan to take my boys on an outing next Friday," he said. "This outing will be our annual picnic and I should like to invite you to come."

"Will Dod and Malcolm be at the outing?" Andy asked eagerly.

"Yes," answered the schoolmaster, "and we should like to have you. What do you say?"

Andy was excited and happy. He turned to his mother and asked, "May I go?"

Mrs. Carnegie smiled. "Of course, Andy. You will enjoy being with the boys."

Then Andy remembered his manners. "I would like very much to come, sir."

After the schoolmaster left, Andy went happily back to work in the garden. He counted the days until Friday and could hardly wait for the big day to come. He would have fun.

Each boy was to take his own lunch on the outing. Mrs. Carnegie packed a good lunch for Andy to carry. She gave him two large chunks of bread with some cheese. Then as a special treat, she baked oatmeal cookies for him to share with the other boys.

"I've put in some extra cookies, Andy," she said with a smile. "Perhaps you can share them with the other boys."

"Thank you, Mother," Andy cried as he waved and rushed out the door.

The boys met Dominie Martin at his school-house, which was not far from Andy's home. With shouts of joy, they set off for the woods on a hillside above the village.

Andy quickly made friends with the other boys. When lunchtime came, he passed around the cookies his mother had made.

Late that afternoon the boys returned to their homes. Andy was sorry to see the day end. He had enjoyed himself with the other boys, and had greatly admired the schoolteacher.

That evening after Mr. Carnegie came from his shop, Andy excitedly told his parents about everything that had happened on the outing. He told about the fun that he had had with the boys. "I like all the boys and I like Dominie Martin, too," he said.

"Aye, lad! I find Dominie Martin very interesting myself," said Mr. Carnegie. "Also your Uncle Lauder says he's a fine teacher."

Andy sat with his knees pulled up to his chin. For several minutes he sat deep in thought. Perhaps Uncle Lauder was right. Maybe he should go to school. Someday he wanted to be somebody—a man people looked up to and admired, as he admired the schoolmaster.

At last he looked up at his parents. "Mother,

62

Father," he said. "May I go to school next fall? I've decided that I would like to go. In fact, I think it will be fun."

Mr. Carnegie smiled and gave Andy a pat on the back. "You've made an important decision, lad," he said. "Now that you've made up your mind, I'm sure that you'll like it."

Mrs. Carnegie looked proudly at Andy. "It's as your father says, Andy. Your decision shows you have a wise head on your shoulders."

It was a cold November evening and a strong wind was blowing outside. Nine-year-old Andy felt cozy and warm as he sat in the sitting room back of Uncle Lauder's shop. The lamps were lighted and there was a pleasant glow from the small fireplace at one side of the room.

Andy's aunt had died a year ago. So now Uncle Lauder in his loneliness spent more and more time with Andy and Dod.

Andy passed many wonderful evenings here with his cousin and uncle. By now he was going to school and always did his homework with his cousin. He loved to read, and depended on Uncle Lauder to help him with his studies. Whenever he had a question, he felt certain that Uncle Lauder could answer it.

Tonight Andy and Dod were seated at a big round table and Uncle Lauder stood leaning against the mantle. With a puzzled frown, Andy looked up from the open book before him. "Uncle Lauder, today the dominie said that England is bigger than Scotland. I think—just this once—that he's mistaken, don't you?"

Dod grinned. "Andy, your pride in Scotland can't change the facts."

Uncle Lauder laughed. "No, Andy," he said. "On the map England is bigger than Scotland. If all the mountains and hills, however, could be rolled out flat, Scotland would be larger than

64

England. But would you want the highlands to be rolled out flat?"

Andy threw back his head and laughed. "No, I wouldn't."

"England has more people than Scotland, too," Dod put in. "For every Scot, there are seven Englishmen."

"Aye, Dod, you're right," Uncle Lauder said with a twinkle in his eyes, "but don't forget, lads—there were greater odds than that against us at the battle of Bannockburn. We fought the English in that famous battle and won. Sometime you'll want to read about it."

From time to time Uncle Lauder told the boys about Scottish history. He taught them to recite poems, famous speeches, and little plays about famous people, which helped them to remember Scottish history.

The boys often made costumes out of paper— crowns for kings and cocked hats and swords for generals. They wore these costumes as they acted the part of heroes by memory. They became so good at memorizing parts in plays that Uncle Lauder rewarded them with a penny for each new play that they learned.

One evening late in December, Andy stayed longer than usual with his cousin Dod. The wind was whirling flakes of snow through the dark street outside the shop. Suddenly the eight o'clock curfew sounded.

When the Abbey bell stopped ringing, Andy knew he must get home as soon as possible. The time at his uncle's had slipped by faster than he realized. He carried a lantern to light his way home through the dark streets.

With a wave of his hand, he left his uncle and Dod. He wound his warm muffler around his throat and ducked his head down against the wind. The wind swung his lantern back and forth as he hurried along the icy street.

"I'll take the short cut home tonight," he said to himself. "I'll go down past the Abbey and through the graveyard."

Suddenly the thought of the lonely graveyard sent chills down his spine. "This is silly," he thought. "Nothing will hurt me."

Leaving the friendly gleams of lamps from the houses behind him, Andy started down the deserted path toward the Abbey. Soon he came to the graveyard and the chills now seemed to have reached his bones. The light from his lantern caused weird shadows to dance here and there in the snowy path.

Despite his determination to be brave, he was more frightened than ever. Soon he could even hear his heart pounding in his body. He began to think of the strange tales often told about ghosts. Such tales were nonsense, his mother had told him. Yet the shadows seemed both alive and frightening.

Andy began to whistle. He felt better when he whistled, but the old stone markers in the cemetery loomed black around him.

Suddenly something caught at one of his legs, causing him to trip and fall. *Yeow!* came a cry close beside him. He shook with fear as he tried to hold on to the lantern.

Andy forgot that people had said there were no such things as ghosts. He felt sure that something unearthly had caught him. Weakly he climbed to his feet and wondered what to do. He wanted to get away as soon as possible, but felt too weak to run.

Yeow! Yeow! The strange cry came again and this time it seemed to be right at his feet. He turned his lantern and the light flickered over a small furry object on the ground. He could scarcely believe his eyes. Here scrambling at his ankle was a small kitten.

"How silly I am!" he thought, ashamed.

He held the lantern low to look more closely at the furry little kitten. As it looked up at him, he could see its eyes gleaming in the orange glow of his lantern. He laughed and picked the kitten up with one hand. Then he cuddled it close to his chest.

"I thought you were a ghost!" he laughed again, "but you were just looking for a friend, along the way." Now he hugged the yellow kitten close to his cheek.

"I'll take you home with me," he said. "The graveyard is not a very warm home for a little kitten. Besides my baby brother Tom will have a lot of fun playing with you."

Happily Andy hurried the rest of the way home, with the kitten snuggled safely under one arm. When he reached the cottage, he rushed in excitedly to show his parents what he had found in the cemetery.

"The kitten needed a home," he said in a rush

of words, "and I thought it would be fun for Tom to play with." Then he told how he had been frightened in the cemetery near the Abbey.

Mr. Carnegie smiled. "It's no shame to admit that you were afraid," he said, "but you'll have to ask your mother about the kitten."

"Oh, may I keep it, Mother?" Andy pleaded.

Mrs. Carnegie glanced at baby Tom's cradle and smiled gently. "Tom is scarcely a year old, but I'm sure he will enjoy the kitten. You may keep it for Tom and yourself, but it looks hungry. Let's give it a saucer of milk and let it sleep close by the fire."

"What are you going to name the kitten, Andy?" his father asked.

Andy thought for a moment. "I think I'll call it Butterball," he said.

Mr. and Mrs. Carnegie agreed that Butterball was a good name for the kitten.

Andy Makes His Pennies Grow

ONE DAY when Andy returned home from school, he found his parents looking closely at something on the table. He leaned over his mother's shoulder to see what it was.

"Why, this is a map of the United States!" he said. "Where did it come from?"

"Your Aunt Aitken sent it to us," his mother explained. "She sent it from her home in Allegheny, Pennsylvania."

"A letter all the way from America!" cried Andy excitedly. Letters were always great news in the Carnegie household. It was seldom that they received letters, especially from all the way across the Atlantic Ocean. The only letters they ever received from America came from Mrs. Carnegie's relatives there.

Aunt Aitkin was Mrs. Carnegie's sister. Besides Aunt Aitken, Mrs. Carnegie had another sister, Aunt Hogan, and a brother, Uncle William, who lived in America. Some years before, they had gone to live in America.

Mrs. Carnegie's sisters and brother greatly missed Scotland, but liked living in America. Uncle William had a good job and was earning a good salary. In Scotland, because times were bad, he would have been poor.

Andy often heard his father talk of the family's hard times. Each year he had found it more difficult to earn a living. Presently he was paid very little for the weaving he did in his shop, and many weavers were out of work. Steam-powered looms in factories could make cloth cheaper and faster.

"May I read the letter?" Andy asked.

"Yes, you certainly may," said Mr. Carnegie handing the closely written pages to Andy. "Your aunt, and Uncle William too, want us to move to America," he added.

Andy's eyes grew round. "A new land—that *would* be adventure. But I just couldn't leave Scotland and Uncle Lauder and Dod and——"

"Just a minute, Andy," interrupted his father. "I didn't say we are *going*." A faraway look came into his eyes. "Not yet, anyway."

Mrs. Carnegie nodded. "Yes, it would be sad to leave our home, but we may have to."

That night as Andy lay in bed, he thought of his aunt's letter. Was it possible that some day his family might move to America? He wondered what living there would be like. Dreaming of life in a new country, he soon fell asleep. The kitten came and curled up at his feet.

As the winter weeks passed, Andy did better

74

and better at school. Reading and doing sums were his favorite studies. Also Uncle Lauder had helped him to become more interested in history. He was proud of all the pennies Uncle Lauder had paid him. By early spring he had earned twenty pennies for memorizing selections from his books.

Andy had carefully saved his pennies in an old sock. Cousin Dod had earned pennies, too, but had spent them for sweets.

"One day I'll make these pennies grow," Andy bragged to his father.

"They won't grow very fast in that old sock of yours," replied Mr. Carnegie.

Andy gave his father a solemn look. "Just wait and see. I'll think of a way."

The gray winter days were followed by gentle spring rains. Baby Tom was able to toddle now on unsteady legs. The kitten had grown round and fat with Andy's good care.

One day Andy went to the butcher's shop for his mother. There, in the little shop, he overheard two housewives talking. They were complaining about the high prices.

"Well, what can I do?" said the butcher, throwing up his hands. "These are hard times. Prices are high because food is scarce. Even rabbits are costly these days. There is nothing I can do to help matters."

Suddenly Andy had an idea. Perhaps he could raise rabbits and sell them to the butcher! Now he could have a business of his own. Here was a chance to make his pennies grow.

Andy's eyes shone with excitement as he told Mr. McDonald, the butcher, of his idea. "I want to raise rabbits to sell you," he said.

Mr. McDonald was short and round, and his stomach shook as he laughed. "Ah, hah! Young Andy, you're a sharp lad. Yes, I'll do business with you, but first you must raise the rabbits."

"I'll bring you the fattest rabbits you've ever had, Mr. McDonald!" Andy bragged.

He was excited with his idea. He thought he could buy a pair of young rabbits from a farmer who lived near Dunfermline. He had seen hutches, or rabbit pens, on the farm. With a pair of rabbits—a male and a female—he could raise baby rabbits.

His mind raced along, making plans. By the time he reached home, he was sure his business could be a success. Eagerly he explained his plan to his mother and showed her the pennies he had saved.

Mrs. Carnegie gave him a gentle smile. "That sounds like a very ambitious business, Andy," she said. "Are you sure that you want to spend your money for rabbits? Something could happen to them, you know. They might run away or die, and then you would lose everything."

For a moment Andy sat thinking of what his

mother had said. "If I work hard and take good care of them," he thought to himself, "surely nothing will happen to them."

"I'm going to risk it, Mother," he announced firmly.

"All right," his mother agreed. "Your father and I will do what we can to help you."

"Thank you, Mother!" Andy cried. He picked up baby Tom and swung him high in the air. "Did you hear what I'm going to do, Tom?" Mrs. Carnegie laughed at Andy's high spirits, and baby Tom gave him a wide grin.

After supper Mr. Carnegie told Andy he would help him build a hutch, or pen, for the rabbits. "Before we start, however, you'd better see whether you can find some rabbits," he added with a twinkle in his eyes.

The following afternoon Andy raced home from school accompanied by Cousin Dod. Hurriedly he explained to his mother that he and

Dod were going out to a farm. They were determined to find some rabbits to bring home.

"Be sure you're back before dark," Mrs. Carnegie warned as Andy picked up his sock of pennies to join Dod at the door.

"We will," the boys answered.

In their excitement the boys ran most of the way to the farm almost a mile away. They started toward the cottage door, but happened to see the farmer coming toward them through the high grass of the pasture.

The farmer walked tall and straight, but he was an old man with a short gray beard, and his face was rough and weatherbeaten. Close by his heels came a large black dog.

"What will you be wanting, lads?" called the farmer in a gruff-sounding voice.

The large dog gave a growl and barked when he caught sight of the boys. Dod was frightened by the dog and stopped where he was. Andy was frightened, too, but walked forward bravely, trying not to show that he was afraid.

"I want to buy a pair of rabbits," he said briefly. "I've seen your hutches and thought you might have rabbits for sale."

The farmer's rough look softened and his eyes smiled as he answered. "Aye, lad, I have rabbits for sale, and I'll sell you a pair for a fair price. I've more than I can feed well for market anyway."

Dod grinned and slapped Andy on the back. "What good luck, Andy!"

Andy too grinned excitedly. "How much are they?" he asked eagerly.

The farmer studied the boys for a minute, and said, "You seem like good lads, willing to work. I'll tell you what I'll do for you. I'll let you have the rabbits as cheaply as I can—ten pennies apiece."

Andy clutched the old sock holding his

pennies. For a moment he hesitated, remembering his mother's words of caution.

"What are you waiting for?" asked Dod.

The farmer turned to go. "It's time to do my chores. I can't make a lower price."

"Wait, please!" cried Andy. "I've no quarrel with the price. Here's the money." He held the sock of pennies toward the farmer.

With a nod, the farmer took the sock and emptied the money into one hand. "Come, lads, I'll fetch the rabbits for you."

Soon the farmer returned with two little brown rabbits. He handed one rabbit to Andy and the other to Dod. The rabbits squirmed and twisted to get away, but the boys held on.

Andy thanked the farmer for letting him have the rabbits. Then the two boys started down the lane carrying the rabbits in their arms. Soon the rabbits quieted down and Andy tucked his rabbit in one of his pockets.

"There," he said, giving the bunny a gentle pat. "You'll be safe in my pocket."

"What are you going to call the rabbits?" asked Dod.

"I'll call this one Tom, after my brother," replied Andy, "and I'll call that one Anna, which is a good name for a girl."

Dod laughed. "Those are strange names for

82

rabbits," he said. "Why don't you call them Brownie and Fluff, or other good names?"

Andy scowled. "I've made up my mind, Dod."

Dod grinned. "All right, Andy," he said. "Once you get your mind set, I know I can't change it. I'll not try."

Soon the boys reached the rough cobblestone streets of the village. Andy walked rapidly and kept ahead of Dod. He wanted to get home as soon as he could to show the bunnies to his parents.

"If we hurry," he said, "maybe we can talk with Father about making a hutch."

Andy Takes a Chance

ANDY and Dod were almost home with the rabbits. Andy pushed his way past housewives, who lingered in small groups to talk or look in the shop windows. He dodged past a hand cart rumbling noisily along the street. Suddenly there came a cry from Dod. "Andy! Andy! Anna is loose. What shall we do?"

They were directly in front of the butcher shop. Andy held fast to the bunny in his pocket. His heart was pounding as he ran to help Dod.

Frightened by the clattering noise of the street, Anna hopped to and fro, looking for a safe place to hide. Dod ran after her frantically,

84

trying to get his hands on her, but she always managed to slip away.

"Head her off, Dod!" called Andy. "Don't let her get out into the street."

Quickly Dod obeyed. He shouted and waved his arms. The men and women on the street stopped to stare at him.

"We must corner her!" cried Andy, catching sight of the butcher's open doorway. He shouted and waved his hands to head her toward the door. Now her only path led straight into the butcher's shop. In a few fast leaps she was inside the room.

Andy and Dod were close at her heels. An old woman was in the shop. When she saw the streak of brown fur, followed by two shouting boys, she began to squeal. Then she dropped her package and held tight to her skirts.

"What is it?" she cried in alarm.

The butcher glared angrily at the boys. "Lads,

out with you," he cried. "Out with you. This is no place to run and play."

Andy did not hear the butcher. His mind was set on catching the runaway rabbit, which soon headed for the back of the shop. On the way she hesitated and he reached down to grab her. Then with a shout of triumph, he caught her and lifted her into his arms.

When the butcher saw that the boys were chasing a rabbit, he gave a hearty laugh. "You surely know that I wouldn't buy a little rabbit like this," he said jokingly.

Andy held tight to the bunnies and grinned. "No, Mr. McDonald," he explained. "We just bought these bunnies in the country and were taking them home, when one called Anna got away. We chased her into your shop to catch her. We're sorry it happened!"

The old woman smoothed her skirts down. "You never know what to expect from young folks these days," she complained. "Of course, there was no real harm done."

Dod hurried to pick up her package and handed it to her with an apology. "I'm sorry, Ma'am, if we frightened you, but we just had to catch the rabbit. Come along, Anna," he added, taking the small creature from Andy. "This time I'll hold you tight."

The boys started on and reached the Carnegie cottage safely. They put the bunnies in an empty corner of the shop. They placed an old chair on the floor to close off the corner so the rabbits couldn't get out.

"Well, now, Andy," said his father, leaving his loom, "we must get busy and build your rabbits a home."

Andy nodded eagerly. "Yes, but where can we get some wood, Father?" he said. "I haven't any money left for buying wood."

Mr. Carnegie's eyes twinkled. "I have a surprise for you, Andy. Come along with me." He led the boys to the rear of the shop. There in a dark corner was a large wooden crate.

"Oh, Father, that will make a wonderful hutch!" Andy cried.

"It will indeed!" Dod added enthusiastically. "Where did you get it?"

"I got it at a factory," explained Mr. Carnegie. "Now let's get busy. I'll need your help to make it into a hutch."

Together the boys helped Mr. Carnegie pull the crate out into an open space on the floor. It was about three feet long and one side had been removed.

"We'll close the open side of the crate with slats," he said. "We'll put the slats close enough together to keep the bunnies in but far enough apart to let in fresh air."

Andy studied the crate for a moment. "We could fasten the slats side by side on a frame.

Then we could use the frame as a door to open the whole front of the hutch. The whole front would be a door."

"That's a good idea, Andy," his father agreed with a nod of his head. "We'll make a door for the front of the hutch."

Dod hurried off to get the slats and some pieces of leather for hinges. Andy brought a saw, hammer, and some nails.

First Mr. Carnegie and the boys made a frame to fit the front of the crate. Then they placed slats side by side on the frame and nailed them in place. At last the front of the hutch was finished.

Mr. Carnegie fastened the door to the top of the hutch with leather hinges so that it could be raised and lowered. He placed a long thin strip of leather at the bottom of the door to be used as a handle.

"In order to lock the hutch," he said, "all you

have to do is tie this thin piece of leather around a nail."

The boys stood back and admired the finished hutch. "Anna and Tom have a fine new home," Andy said enthusiastically. "I hope they'll be happy here."

Later Mr. Carnegie and the boys carried the hutch out to the garden at the rear of the cottage. They gathered a few stones and put them in place to make a foundation. Then they lifted the hutch onto the foundation.

"Now," he said at last, "the bottom of the hutch will stay dry. Had we put the hutch on the ground, the rabbits would be sure to get wet feet when it rains." He laughed.

Andy could hardly wait to put the bunnies in their new home. He and Dod gathered some long dry grass and put it on the floor of the hutch. "That will make a nice soft bed for them," he said confidently.

90

"They're probably hungry by now," suggested Dod. "What are you going to feed them?"

"Well, I'm sure they like tender green weeds or leaves," said Andy. "Let's pull some greens at the back of the garden."

Soon the boys collected several large bunches of greens and put them in the hutch. Then Andy filled an old bowl with water and put it in the hutch beside the greens.

"Now, let's get Anna and Tom!" he said.

The boys rushed to the shop to get Anna and Tom. They placed the rabbits in the hutch and locked the door with the leather string.

The rabbits nibbled eagerly at the tender green leaves. They twitched their noses and hopped about inside the crate.

"I think they like their new home, Andy," Dod said with a grin.

Andy nodded happily. He felt very proud as he looked at the rabbits in the hutch. Now

his rabbits were safe and well fed. And he was in business for himself!

The weeks passed and gradually spring gave way to warm sunny summer days. Andy enjoyed his rabbits and could almost see them grow. Each day they seemed to be bigger, and they needed more and more to eat.

Before long Andy had fed the rabbits all the weeds out of his mother's garden. He dared not feed them any of the vegetables from the garden. Each day he made a trip to a woods near the village. There he gathered berries and greens and tender young grass.

Soon Andy realized that he needed help in gathering enough food for the rabbits. "I must think of a better way to get food for them," he said to himself. Suddenly, one day, he thought of a plan that he thought would work.

"I can't gather enough food by myself," he told Dod, "but I have an idea. If four or five of us were to gather food together, we could get enough to feed the rabbits for a week!"

"Maybe you're right, Andy," Dod agreed, "but what boys would be willing to spend their time gathering food for rabbits?"

"A few of the neighbor lads," replied Andy.

Dod looked puzzled and shook his head. "The lads won't work for nothing, and you can't pay them," he said.

Andy laughed. "Oh, yes, I can, Dod."

Dod listened to Andy's eager explanation. Each boy would spend one morning a week gathering food. Then later each would have a tiny rabbit named after him.

"You're taking a chance, Andy," Dod cautioned. "After all, you don't have any baby rabbits yet—and maybe you never will!"

Andy was sure that he could persuade the boys to work, and he was right. He found three boys who were willing to gather food for the rabbits. In return he promised to name a bunny after each one of them. One day in August weeks later, he went to feed the rabbits. There, in the hutch, he found a litter of tiny bunnies.

Gently, with one finger, he stroked their warm bare sides. He counted five bunnies in all. One would be named Malcolm, one Robby, one Jamie, and one Dod.

"The last one I'll name for myself! Just wait until Dod hears the good news!"

Andy Goes to Crossgates

UNCLE LAUDER bowed his head and gave a sigh. "Lads, I don't know what to do!" he said.

He was speaking to Andy and Dod in the greengrocer shop. He pointed to baskets of gooseberries stacked in one corner. Then he picked up a few berries in his hand. With another sigh, he let them drop through his fingers and back into a basket.

"Here are a hundred pints of gooseberries too ripe to keep more than a day. I'll never be able to sell them by tomorrow night. What a loss of money!"

Andy popped a berry into his mouth. "They

taste good," he said. "Surely you can sell them before they spoil."

Uncle Lauder shrugged his shoulders and went back to work. "I can't blame anyone but myself," he said. "I ordered these berries from Farmer McNeil a few days ago, but I didn't expect the hot August weather would ripen them so soon. When he delivered them this morning I couldn't go back on my word."

Dod and Andy nodded approval. "You surely treated him fairly," they said.

Uncle Lauder explained that he probably would lose every cent he had paid for the berries. "Unless——" he started to say.

"Unless what, Father?" Dod inquired.

"I had an idea but it wouldn't work," Uncle Lauder answered vaguely. "Besides I couldn't get away to go to Crossgates."

Andy looked again at the baskets of berries. Then he looked eagerly at Uncle Lauder. "What idea did you have, Uncle Lauder? Is there some way we can help you?"

Uncle Lauder gave Andy a broad smile and patted him on the shoulder. "Well, if I could take the berries to the market at Crossgates, I probably could sell them. But I can't leave the shop for a whole day."

Andy's mind worked quickly. Uncle Lauder couldn't leave the shop to go to Crossgates, but he and Dod could! He was sure that they could sell the berries. After all, he had sold some rabbits—and for a nice profit, too.

Eagerly he asked Uncle Lauder whether he and Dod could go. What an adventure they would have. They would be all on their own.

At first Uncle Lauder shook his head and said that the boys couldn't go, but the boys didn't give up. Dod pleaded and Andy argued that even if they failed, it wouldn't be any worse than letting the berries spoil in the store.

"Your head surely works when it comes to matters of business, Andy," Uncle Lauder said at last. "Perhaps I should let you and Dod see what you can do. I'll keep twenty-five pints here and you boys may take the rest—seventy-five pints. I'll be greatly surprised, however, if you manage to sell *all* of them."

Andy and Dod danced about and clapped each other excitedly on the shoulders. "Just you wait and see, Uncle Lauder!" exclaimed Andy. "We'll sell all your berries and come home with our pockets full of money!"

Uncle Lauder arranged for a neighbor to take the berries to Crossgates. He would bring his cuddy cart around to the shop at dawn the next morning. The cuddy cart was a small two-wheel cart pulled by a donkey.

Bright-eyed and eager to get started, Andy came to the shop early the next morning. Dod, yawning, opened the shop door to let him in.

The two boys worked hard to load the cuddy
cart with berries.

Uncle Lauder came out to say good-by to the
boys. "Do a good job, lads, and I'll give you
three pennies apiece."

Andy shouted and waved his cap in the air.
"We'll sell all of them, Uncle Lauder!"

The neighbor took up the reins and started
to drive the cuddy cart slowly down the street.
Dod and Andy walked along behind the cart,
talking and laughing.

Soon they left the village and followed the
dusty road leading eastward. Crossgates lay
three miles east of Dunfermline. It was smaller
than Dunfermline, but was an important center
because several roads met there from nearby
villages. One road came from the Firth of Forth,
where there was a ferry that traveled back and
forth to Edinburgh.

The sun was shining brightly now above the

horizon. The sturdy donkey pulled the cuddy cart along the rutted road at a slow, steady pace. From time to time the driver dozed and nodded, but Andy and Dod laughed and sang loudly as they walked along behind.

They crossed over a hill beyond which they could see Crossgates. As they came close to the village, they met many carts and wagons. Some were loaded with vegetables and grains grown on farms. Others were loaded with flour which had been ground in nearby mills.

Soon the cuddy cart was rattling over the cobblestones of the street. "Hi, Andy!" shouted Dod excitedly. "We're in Crossgates. We're in Crossgates. We're here!"

Eagerly Andy viewed the crowded main street of the village. There were fewer shops than in Dunfermline, but many more carts and wagons. It was hard to drive the cuddy cart along the crowded street.

A worried look came to Dod's face. "Now that we're here, what shall we do?"

Andy looked around confidently. "We'll stop the cart here and start to sell, just as the other men are doing."

There was only one tiny greengrocer shop in the village. The housewives did most of their buying from the carts and wagons that lined the street. Not far from Andy's cart was an old man selling eggs from a cart.

"Come on, Dod, let's get busy," said Andy with enthusiasm. He lifted a big basket of ber-ries from the cuddy cart. Dod grabbed a wooden scoop, which Uncle Lauder had said they could use to measure the berries. This wooden scoop held exactly one pint.

"Fine ripe gooseberries for sale!" Andy called to the passersby.

"Gooseberries! Gooseberries for sale!" Dod called in the other direction.

Housewives began to stop at the cart to look at the berries. One woman bought five pints of berries, which she poured into a large bowl. Another woman bought two pints, which she put into her market basket.

The women liked the berries and were happy to be able to buy them at such a low price. They felt that Andy and Dod were giving them a bargain on the berries.

The boys grinned as they put pennies into their pockets. Their cheeks glowed pink with the thrill and excitement of making sales.

At the end of a half hour, Andy looked at the berries still in the cart. "I wonder how many pints we've already sold," he said. He began to count, "Five, seven, eight, ten—thirty-one, thirty-two, thirty-three. We've sold thirty-three pints already," he announced.

Dod nodded. "Yes, but we still have an awful lot left, Andy."

Andy knew that Dod was right. "Don't worry," he said. "We'll sell them—every pint."

With fresh enthusiasm the boys began to call out again to the housewives crowding the street. Suddenly there came a clatter of hoofs on the cobblestones down the street. "Stop him! Stop him!" cried a woman.

People scattered and ran for protection as the clatter of hoofs grew louder. Andy dashed out into the street to see what was going on. Dod followed close at his heels.

There, heading straight for them, was a runaway pony, pulling an empty cart. The cart swayed dangerously from side to side, almost tipping over. First it grazed the front of a shop. Then it narrowly missed locking wheels with a wagon loaded with vegetables to sell. The pony was frightened and galloped on, despite attempts to halt him.

"Andy, get out of the way!" Dod cried, jumping back. "Look out. You'll get run over if you don't get back!"

Andy paid no heed to Dod's warning. Instead, he ran right out into the street toward the pony. "I've got to stop him," he thought. "He might hurt someone, or ram our cart of berries. He's headed straight this way."

Just then the pony swerved and headed toward the old man's cart loaded with eggs. Andy put on an extra burst of speed and leaped forward. He grabbed the reins near the pony's mouth and held on as tightly as possible.

"Whoa, boy, whoa!" he called, trying hard to stop the frightened pony, but he was only dragged forward. The pony gave a big lurch to one side, but he managed to hold on. Then suddenly the pony came to a stop just a few feet from the cart loaded with eggs.

At once a crowd gathered around Andy. He calmed the pony by stroking its neck.

A man clapped him on the shoulder. "You're a spunky lad. 'Twas a brave thing you did."

"Aye, aye," the others agreed.

A young woman pushed her way through the crowd to Andy. "Ah, that pony of mine," she said. "Thank you, laddie, for stopping him. I don't know what got into him. I left him for just a minute or so while I shopped. And it was then he took it into his head to run away."

Andy grinned and pushed his tousled blond hair back from his eyes. "Well, I could see that he needed stopping, but he seemed to be having a grand time."

The crowd chuckled. The woman took the reins from Andy and held out two pennies to reward him for stopping the pony. "These are all I have left," she said. "Take them as a small reward for what you have done."

Andy's cheeks turned pink.

"Aye, lad, you deserve a reward from me,

too," said the old man with the cart of eggs. He held out five pennies toward Andy.

Andy shook his head. "I can't take any money for what I have done, but I can sell you some nice ripe gooseberries."

There were more chuckles from the people standing about. "There's a lad who is quick to take advantage of an opportunity," said a man. "I'll take some berries, boy."

"And I," said a housewife.

One by one others in the group agreed to buy berries. They stepped up to get them as fast as Andy and Dod could measure them out and take in the money. Soon every pint was gone.

Dod gave Andy a playful poke on the arm. "Look, Andy! We've sold every pint! Will my father ever be surprised!"

Andy proudly jingled the coins in his pockets. "We've taken in a bit of spending money, too. Let's hurry home and tell what happened."

Andy Goes on a Long Journey

THE WINTER of 1847-1848 brought more hard times to the Carnegies. The lines of worry around Mr. Carnegie's eyes deepened and the family had scarcely any money to spend.

There now was a large factory in town, where weaving was done by machines. Many weavers had no work, because the machines at the factory could do their work faster.

Many weavers had moved away from the village to larger cities where they could find work in factories. A few, like Mr. Carnegie, still worked their hand looms, but it was difficult to sell hand-woven cloths. These cloths were high because it cost more to make them. One machine could do the work of many men.

One by one Mr. Carnegie had to sell his looms and let his workers go. Now he had only one loom left and most of the time this one loom was idle. The Carnegies moved to a smaller house on Moody Street, near the house where Andy had been born. They had only one tiny room to live in above the shop.

Mrs. Carnegie's brother, Tom Morrison, was a shoemaker in the village. While times were hard, Uncle Tom let Mrs. Carnegie sew shoes for him to earn a few pennies a week. She needed the money to help feed the family.

All shoes were made by hand. So far there were no machines for making shoes. For this reason, even though times were hard, Uncle Tom could still earn a living at his trade.

One night twelve-year-old Andy sat near his mother by the fireside. He threaded the large needles for her as she sewed the new shoes. Four-year-old Tom was fast asleep in his small bed in the far corner of the room. Mr. Carnegie had gone off on an errand.

Suddenly Andy broke the silence. "Mother, I want to earn some money, too. I'm growing up and it isn't right for you to work so hard, when I do nothing at all."

Mrs. Carnegie looked at him and smiled. He was stocky and well built, but shorter than most boys of his age.

"You already help here at home," said Mrs. Carnegie with a nod. "Besides, your real job now is to go to school and to learn."

"But, Mother, I can do more. Why don't we start a store here at home? There would be enough space in Father's shop."

"What would we sell?" Mrs. Carnegie asked with a twinkle in her eyes. "Would we sell rabbits or gooseberries?"

Andy laughed at his mother's joke, but he thought starting a store was a good idea. He talked with his father and Uncle Lauder about it. His father suggested that they could make sweets to sell. Uncle Lauder suggested that they sell vegetables from Mrs. Carnegie's garden. He offered to help by giving them sugar, flour, and tea from his own store.

"Then," he explained, "you can start a real greengrocer shop like mine. You can pay me back out of the profits."

Andy's eyes sparkled with excitement. "Oh, let us try it, Father."

Andy's father gave his permission, and a few days later Andy and his mother opened the shop for business. There were screw pokes, or sweets, for the children, and there were cabbages, carrots, and potatoes.

As the cold winter days passed, Andy worked hard. He ran all the shop errands. Once a week he delivered potatoes and fresh tea to old Widow McPherson on Green Street who always looked forward to seeing him.

Often his customers couldn't pay right away for their groceries, but he had a quick mind for figures. He always remembered what each person owed. At the end of the week he would collect what was owed.

"Andy, how do you remember what Widow McPherson owes you?" asked Dod. "How do you remember what all the others owe you?"

Andy grinned. "I don't know, Dod, but I like to add and subtract. Remembering figures is a sort of game for me."

Andy worked hard and long through the gray days of winter, but there was still barely enough money for the family. Each month Mr. Carnegie sold less cloth than he had before.

One day in February, Andy started home from school. He ran most of the way, because he wanted to make some deliveries. Breathless, he swung open the shop door.

His brother Tom was quietly sitting near the fireplace, drawing pictures on an old slate. His father held a letter which he was discussing with Mrs. Carnegie.

As Andy looked at his parents, he sensed that they were much more excited than usual. "Do we have a letter from Aunt Aitken or Aunt Hogan?" he asked eagerly.

"Aye, lad—from both," his father answered.

"Both?" Andy was surprised. Usually their letters came singly and sometimes weeks apart.

"Yes, both." His mother had a faraway look. "They want us to come to America."

Andy shouted. "Hooray! A visit to America! That will be great fun."

"Not a visit, lad," stated his father. "They want us to come live there."

Andy stared at his parents. He loved Scotland.

114

It was hard to imagine leaving it. "But—but this is our home," he said.

Mrs. Carnegie looked at Andy's puzzled face. "Sometimes for our own good, Andy, we must choose a way that hurts," she said. "Your father and I have been thinking of moving to America for a long, long time."

Mr. Carnegie nodded. "Aye, Andy, you understand how hard times are here in Scotland. America is a land of many opportunities—a country where a man can find work. Your mother and I think it would be a good place for you and Tom to grow up." He smiled and winked at Andy. "Why, if you work as hard there as you have here, you might grow up to be rich and famous!"

"Me, too?" asked Tom suddenly.

Everyone laughed. "Yes, you too," said Mrs. Carnegie, giving Tom a hug.

The Carnegies hoped to take a ship to the

United States in May, but lacked enough money to pay their passage. They had only a fraction of the money they would need for the trip. Mr. Carnegie tried to find work to earn money, but could find very little to do.

One day in April, Mrs. Carnegie's good friend, Ailie Fargie, came into the little greengrocer shop. She knew how badly the Carnegies wanted to go to America and offered to lend them money from her savings. The Carnegies disliked to borrow money from her, but felt there was no other way. They were grateful for her offer and promised to pay her back.

Within a few weeks they sold all their furniture and dishes at an auction, or public sale, but obtained very little money from the auction. They closed the greengrocer shop and collected the clothes and other things they wanted to take with them. Soon they had everything packed in shabby satchels and bags.

Early the next morning the Carnegies started on their long journey. Uncle Lauder, Dod, and Uncle Tom came along to see them off.

As the family left Dunfermline behind, Andy felt very sad. He realized that he might never see his old home again and fought hard to keep back the tears. Soon he turned to catch one last glimpse of the great Abbey and the town. There, shining in the morning sun, he saw the big stone letters at the top of the Abbey tower.

"King Robert the Bruce," he read. Suddenly the tower was out of sight, hidden by the hills leading down to the Firth of Forth.

At the Firth, six miles from Dunfermline, Andy and his family boarded a small ferry boat for Edinburgh. The boat ride across the Firth was very pleasant, but Andy didn't enjoy the trip. All the while, he wanted to turn back.

He felt too old to cry, yet he had a strange empty feeling in his stomach that he couldn't get rid of. He had never had such a terrible feeling before.

At Edinburgh the Carnegies boarded a small canal boat, which would take them to Glasgow. There they would board a sailing boat, which would take them on their voyage to America.

For nearly fifty miles they traveled westward across Scotland by canal. Uncle Lauder and Uncle Tom laughed and joked—to cheer up the lads, they said. They told tales of the Scottish heroes who had fought in the countryside along the winding canal.

As the men talked, Andy's spirits began to rise. Soon he imagined he could see the kilted clansmen roving about and hear some of the bagpipes playing. The stories which his uncles told helped him to forget his grief.

Early on May 19, 1848, the Carnegies departed in a sailing ship from Glasgow. Their ship was named the "Wiscassett."

"Aye, it looks sturdy enough," said Uncle
Tom. He leaned on his walking stick and admired the great sailing ship.

Andy looked up at Uncle Tom. As always, his

uncle wore a frock coat and black top hat. He was a very imposing figure.

"Was this ship built in Scotland?" asked Andy.

"No, lad, it was built in America—in Maine," answered Uncle Tom.

"Aye, Andy," said Uncle Lauder. "Once it was a whaling ship, but now it has been changed into a merchant ship to carry goods and passengers from here to America."

"A whaling ship!" Dod cried. He thumped Andy on the back. "You're certainly lucky. I bet I'll never have a chance to sail on a whaler."

Andy shook his head. "I'd rather stay in Scotland." He felt tears coming to his eyes.

Two sailors carried the Carnegies' luggage aboard the ship. Mrs. Carnegie kissed Uncle Tom and Uncle Lauder good-by, and gave Dod a final hug and kiss.

Soon she took Tom's hand and walked up the wooden gangplank that led from the dock to the ship. Mr. Carnegie bade Dod and the two men farewell. Then he told Andy it was time to go.

As Andy looked at his uncles and Dod, the tears rolled down his cheeks. He raced over to Uncle Lauder and threw his arms around him.

"I cannot leave—I cannot leave!"

"Come, lad!" Mr. Carnegie called.

A sailor was working nearby, loosening the ropes that held the ship fast to the wharf. With a kindly smile he walked over to Andy and pulled him from Uncle Lauder.

"There, boy," he said. "Aboard with you now. We must be off with the tide. When we get to sea you can help my mates and me sail the ship." He led Andy up the gangplank.

"Cast off!" came the orders.

The sailors ran to obey and, pulling ropes over squeaking pulleys, raised the great sails. Then the schooner swung away from the wharf, and Andy took a long last look at Scotland.

Andy Has a Dream

ANDY and his family were weary but happy when they reached their new home in America in Allegheny, Pennsylvania. They had traveled for three months before they reached Allegheny. The Carnegies were going to settle here, because this was where Aunt Aitken and Uncle and Aunt Hogan lived in America. The day the Carnegies arrived Aunt Aitken and Uncle and Aunt Hogan were on hand to meet them.

The new city seemed rough, noisy, and dirty to Andy. Most of the streets were unpaved, and either dusty or muddy. Most of the houses which lined the streets on either side were made of wood. They seemed flimsy and ramshackle after the sturdy stone cottages of Dunfermline. The roofs consisted of wooden shingles instead of colorful red tiles as in Dunfermline.

Uncle and Aunt Hogan lived on Rebecca Street, near the Allegheny River. On the other side of the river was the city of Pittsburgh. Many heavily laden flatboats and large rafts of lumber floated down the river.

"What do the flatboats carry, Uncle Hogan?" Andy wanted to know.

"They carry coal, Andy," said Uncle Hogan. "Pennsylvania is noted for coal. The flatboats carry coal to other cities."

The Hogans lived in a two-story frame house, but had a smaller house at the back on an alley. They told the Carnegies that they could move into this little house and make it their home. Andy and the others carried their belongings into the house and put them in place.

"You must have supper with us," Aunt Hogan said cheerfully to Mrs. Carnegie. "This is your first night in your new home."

Andy put on his best clothes—the ones he had worn to school in Dunfermline. Tom begged to be allowed to wear his Scottish kilt. Kilts were worn only on festive days in Scotland, but Mrs. Carnegie agreed, and soon Tom was dressed in his fine Scottish kilt. Andy had a Scottish kilt too, but he felt much more comfortable dressed in school clothes.

"May we go out and look around, Mother, while you and Father get ready?" asked Andy. "We won't go far from the house."

With a nod Mrs. Carnegie let the boys go, and they raced from the house into the street. Then they walked along a narrow board sidewalk in front of the Hogan house.

Suddenly Andy and Tom heard shouts of laughter and looked down the walk. There, a few houses away, were two boys. The boys were laughing loudly and pointing at Tom.

"Andy, what's so funny?" asked Tom.

Andy looked at the boys in surprise. They seemed to be about his age, but were somewhat taller and heavier.

The boys drew closer and kept pointing toward Tom. "Hey, who's your little friend with skirts on?" one of them asked.

Andy's face grew red with anger. "Don't you know a fine Scotch kilt when you see one?"

"Listen to him," the other boy said. "What a funny accent!"

Andy didn't wait to hear any more. He lunged at the boys, throwing his fists about wildly. Tom jumped up and down shouting, "Hit them, Andy —and knock them down!"

Soon Andy hit one of the boys and down he went. "Wait, wait!" called the other boy. He laughed and held fast to one of Andy's arms.

By this time the first boy had climbed to his feet. "Yes, calm down, Scotty," he said. "We were only teasing to see what you would do."

"That's all," said the other boy. "Our folks came from Scotland, too, but we were born in

America. I guess all my dad's bragging about the fighting Scotch spirit is true."

Soon Andy's face took on a grin. "We're going to be your new neighbors," he said. "Maybe we'll find you all right—since your parents came from Scotland."

Just then Mr. Carnegie called to Andy and Tom. Andy brushed his clothes quickly and smoothed the hair out of his eyes. Tom waited and finally gave Andy a tug on the arm. "Come on, Andy, we'd better go," he said.

Tom and Andy waved at the two strange boys and ran to answer their father's call. The two boys smiled broadly and waved back. "We'll see you around soon," they said as they turned and ran off down the street.

Suddenly Tom's face took on a thoughtful look. "Maybe, Andy," he said, "since we live in America, I shouldn't wear my kilt!"

Andy laughed as he looked down at Tom and

put one arm around him. "Well, we are going to be Americans now. I suppose we should try to be a part of our new country."

Within a few months Mr. Carnegie obtained work at the Blackstock Cotton Mills. Mrs. Carnegie, too, found work, binding shoes at home in the evenings. Tom entered an American school, but Andy insisted on going to work.

"I'll get my schooling somehow or other," he promised his parents, "but first I want to do my part to help out."

Andy's parents agreed. Andy was proud to have them treat him as a grown-up. He knew that they would need every penny possible to get started here in America. Without his help, they might not be able to send Tom to school.

One sunny fall day Andy came running home, breathless with excitement. "I have a job—I have a job!" he shouted as he threw open the door and rushed inside.

His mother smiled. "Good, Andy!" she said. "What kind of job do you have?"

"I'm going to be a bobbin boy at the cotton mill where Father works," replied Andy. "My wages will be one dollar and twenty cents a week! Isn't that something?"

The next morning while it was still dark, Andy got up to walk to work with his father. He carried some bread and cheese to eat for lunch. All day long he worked hard at his job and by evening he was worn out. He could scarcely keep up with his father as they walked home through the dimly lighted streets.

Week after week Andy worked in the mill. He found the work boring and was always glad to return home at the end of the day. His mother usually had warm soup waiting for him for supper, and her happy smiles and words of encouragement made him feel good.

One day Andy was offered a job in another

factory where he would earn forty-five cents more a week. In his new job he would have to look after the engine and boiler in the cellar and dip bobbins in a vat of oil. He quickly agreed to take the job. His family needed every extra penny he could earn.

Andy had problems on the new job. He found it difficult to fire the furnace and keep the right amount of steam in the boiler. Also the oil where he dipped the bobbins had an unpleasant odor that made him sick.

Sometimes the workers upstairs complained about Andy's work. They said that he wasn't putting enough fuel in the furnace to keep up steam. At the same time Andy knew that he had to be careful about getting the steam too high. When the boiler began to hiss the pressure was becoming too high. If it went still higher, the boiler might explode.

Grimly Andy worked at the job. He was very

unhappy, but felt that he just couldn't fail his family. Most of all he was worried about the pressure of the steam in the boiler. Each day he feared that the boiler would burst and blow up the factory.

One winter night Andy tossed and turned in his bed. Suddenly he shouted, "It's going to burst! It's going to burst!"

Tom sat up and rubbed his eyes. "What's going to burst?" he asked.

"The boiler—the boiler!" shouted Andy. "The boiler at the factory."

Tom gave Andy a shake and said, "Wake up, Andy. You are dreaming."

Slowly Andy opened his eyes. He felt a bit shaky and there were beads of perspiration on his forehead.

"Are you sick, Andy?" asked Tom. "You were almost shouting in your sleep."

"No, Tom, I'm not sick," Andy answered,

slowly shaking his head. "I was just having a bad dream, that's all."

"What about?"

Andy shivered as he recalled his dream. "About the boiler at the factory."

"You're working too hard," said Tom with an earnest look on his face. "Why don't you quit working and go to school? We can get along without the money."

Suddenly Andy grinned. "No, I won't quit work regardless of what happens," he said. "I've had a little schooling. Now you must have a chance to get yours."

"Aw, Andy!" Tom frowned. "I really wish you would quit so we could go to school together."

Andy was firm. "No, but you can help me in another way, if you wish," he said.

"How?" asked Tom eagerly.

"By not telling about my bad dream," replied Andy. "Mother would worry if she knew about

132

the boiler and Father already has worries of his own. One of these days I'll get a job that I like better. And when I find it, I'll make sure that you're the first to know."

Tom smiled. "All right, Andy. I promise not to tell Mother and Father about your dream. In return don't forget your promise to me."

Andy ruffled Tom's hair in a brotherly manner. Then the boys pulled the warm soft quilts up over them and fell fast asleep.

Andy Wins His Chance

ONE COLD winter night there was a knock at the door of the Carnegie home. "Who could be coming to the door so late?" asked Andy.

Mrs. Carnegie opened the door, and there stood Uncle Hogan. "Why, Ben, come in," she cried. "Let me take your coat and muffler."

"Thank you, Margaret," said Uncle Hogan, taking off his coat and pulling the muffler from around his neck. "It's a bitter cold night out, but I just had to stop in with a message for Andy. I've been playing checkers with Dave Brooks who manages the new telegraph office in Pittsburgh. I told him I'd stop."

Everybody wondered what message Uncle Hogan had for Andy, but nobody asked questions. Then Uncle Hogan went on. "Dave Brooks is an old friend of mine and a great checker player. We've been playing checkers together for many years."

"Yes, but what does that have to do about a message for me?" interrupted Andy. "Please tell me what he said."

Uncle Hogan smiled. "Dave told me tonight that he needs a new telegraph boy—a boy to deliver messages, and I told him about you. He said that if you're interested, he will talk with you about it tomorrow morning."

Andy could scarcely believe his ears. For almost a year now he had looked after the boiler and engine at the bobbin factory. He had been very unhappy there, but had stuck it out, hoping things would be better. Now, at last, a great new opportunity had come his way.

Andy's father shook his head. "I'm afraid that Andy's too small for that kind of a job. He's too small to run about the city with important messages. Besides, he doesn't know the streets of the city."

"Let me try, Father," cried Andy. "I can learn the streets of the city. And the pay is two dollars and fifty cents a week!"

"Please, please, Father, let Andy try," pleaded young Tom.

Suddenly everyone seemed to start talking at once. Andy's mother felt that Andy should talk with Mr. Brooks, and Uncle Hogan felt talking could do no harm. Finally, Mr. Carnegie gave in and agreed to let Andy go to talk about the job with Mr. Brooks.

Andy's eyes shone as he dreamed of holding a position with the telegraph company. The telegraph, he knew, had been invented about ten years before. Up to that time, there had been no fast way of sending messages long distance. Now a message could be sent many miles in a matter of minutes. When a message was received at the telegraph office, it was written down. Then a boy carried it as fast as he could to the person to whom it was addressed.

After Uncle Hogan left, Mrs. Carnegie set to work on Andy's Sunday-best clothes. She washed and ironed his white linen shirt and brushed his navy blue jacket and pants.

"Here you are, Andy," she said at last, handing him his clothes. "Now you'll look very neat when you go to see Mr. Brooks."

"Thank you, Mother, for helping me," said Andy. He realized that Mr. Brooks would want his messenger boy to look attractive as well as be able to think and act well.

Bright and early the next morning Andy got ready to make his trip to Pittsburgh. His father insisted on going with him.

"I'm not wholly in favor of your going," he said, "but I'll go with you just to be sure you can find the telegraph office."

Andy was confident he could find the office by himself, but he knew better than to argue with his father. "I'll not object to Father's going with me, but I want to talk with Mr. Brooks by myself," he thought. He was happy and sure of himself—sure that he could get the job and handle it well afterwards.

Andy and his father set out for their long walk to the office in Pittsburgh. His spirits were very high as he walked along beside his father in the bright crisp winter weather.

Soon they crossed the bridge to Pittsburgh and in no time at all, it seemed to Andy, reached the corner of Wood and Fourth Streets. The telegraph office was located here, on the second floor of the corner building.

The business offices along the street were

opening for the day. Men hurried along both sides of the street on their way to work. Andy and his father stopped to talk for a moment on the sidewalk. Suddenly a boy several years older than Andy came dashing out a door. He looked neither to the right nor to the left and ran straight into Andy before he could stop. Then he started to run on.

"Sorry, kid," the boy called over his shoulder as he raced down the street.

Andy's face turned red and he clenched his fists. The boy's tone had been insulting, and Andy didn't like to be called a kid. He turned to shout at the boy, but suddenly stopped and looked at his father. "I guess this would be a poor day to fight."

Mr. Carnegie laughed. "Aye, Andy. A black eye would not give Mr. Brooks a very good impression. Now run along, lad."

Andy gave his father a quick grin. "Thank

you, Father," he said. "I'll look for you here after I see Mr. Brooks."

Mr. Carnegie nodded and Andy opened the door to go inside. He walked upstairs to an office where a door stood ajar. Inside he could see a counter with several chairs and a table behind it. On one end of the table there was a complicated-looking machine with a roll of paper tape at one end. On the far side of the room was a door with words on the door which read "Mr. Brooks, Manager."

The door opened and a man appeared with some papers in his hands. He gave Andy a quick look and beckoned him to come in. "You must be young Andrew Carnegie," he said.

Suddenly Andy felt at ease. Mr. Brooks had a kindly look about him, and started at once to show Andy about the office. He pointed to the telegraph machine on the table and explained what it was and how it worked.

140

"That large machine," he said, "is our receiving instrument. When a message comes in over the wires, it prints dots and dashes on paper. Then the clerk, or copyist, translates the message into the letters."

Mr. Brooks took Andy into his office and asked him several questions. He listened closely as Andy answered the questions and described the work he had done in the past.

"Please, sir, all I want is a chance," said Andy. "I'm small and don't know the streets of the city, but I'll learn them."

Mr. Brooks nodded. "I believe you," he said. "When can you go to work?"

Andy's eyes shone. "Right now!" he cried.

"George!" Mr. Brooks called to a boy in the office outside. "Come in here."

Andy turned and saw the same boy who had bumped into him downstairs. "Yes, Mr. Brooks," the boy answered. "What can I do?"

Mr. Brooks introduced Andy to George. "This is Andy Carnegie," he said cheerfully. "I've decided to hire Andy to help you deliver telegrams here in the city. Take him under your wing and teach him the ropes."

George stared at Andy and seemed to be surprised. "I'll gladly teach him, but he's rather small for the job," he said.

Andy wanted to shout angry words at George, but he held his tongue. "I'll show him," he thought to himself. "I'll keep up with him—and maybe more!"

Mr. Brooks laughed good-naturedly. "Well, Andy thinks he can do the work, and we'll give him a chance." Then he sent the boys into the outer office to start working.

Andy was proud that he had been given the telegraph job. He was so happy and determined that he almost forgot about his father who was waiting for him on the street below.

Quickly Andy ran down and told his father that he had been hired. With a nod, Mr. Carnegie started back home.

Andy started to work and soon won George's respect and confidence. His greatest problem at first was to learn the names of the streets in Pittsburgh. Also he needed to learn the addresses of important business places.

Every night at home Andy studied the names of the streets and business places of the city. He made lists of the main business streets and the main business places located on the streets. Then he studied them until he could name the streets and business places in order as he would come to them.

Mr. Brooks was pleasantly surprised by the speed with which Andy learned. In a short time Andy knew almost as much about the city as George did. Not only that, he pleased people and they were glad to see him.

During the succeeding weeks as Andy delivered messages, he became acquainted with many important businessmen. He called them by name when he met them on the street, and they complimented him on his remarkable memory. Soon he became a familiar figure to the downtown business district of Pittsburgh.

Andy continued to work hard and Mr. Brooks was greatly pleased. The telegraph office expanded and carried on more and more work. Soon there were more telegrams than the two boys could deliver by themselves.

One day Mr. Brooks asked Andy whether he knew of another boy who would be interested in a messenger's job. "I want a boy willing to work like you," he added with a smile.

Andy was proud of Mr. Brooks' praise. He said he knew just the boy for the job—Robert Pitcairn, who was one of his friends in the Rebecca Street neighborhood.

Robert proved to be a good worker, as Andy had recommended him to be. Soon the business expanded and Mr. Brooks asked Andy to recommend other boys for messengers. He recommended two other boys and they proved to be good workers, too. Mr. Brooks was pleased.

All the boys in the office worked hard, but they got along well together. George, who at first thought Andy was too small for the job, became one of Andy's best friends. Often they joked about the time George bumped into Andy when Andy first came to see Mr. Brooks.

Andy Delivers Telegrams

We're going to have a visitor," George said excitedly to the boys in the office.

"What visitor?" asked all the boys crowding around to listen.

"Mr. Reid, the big boss—the superintendent," said George. "He will visit us sometime tomorrow, probably tomorrow morning."

"Wow!" cried Andy. "We really must be on our good behavior!"

"That's right, Andy," laughed Mr. Brooks, as he came from his office. "Mr. Reid's visit will be routine, but he'll give us a close look while he is here. Demonstrate good manners, dress neatly, and be ready for inspection. Try to look your best when you come tomorrow."

The following day Andy was the first to arrive at the office. He started to work at once to straighten up the office and to make it inviting. He swept the bare floor and brushed down a few cobwebs in the corners of the room.

He straightened stacks of newspapers and other papers which Mr. Brooks kept on hand. He worked quietly and tried not to interfere with the work of the telegraph operator, whose desk was on the far side of the room.

Soon George and the other boys arrived. Their faces were freshly scrubbed, their hair was neatly brushed, and their clothes carefully pressed. They were ready for inspection.

"Good morning, boys," Mr. Brooks called as he entered the office. Following close behind him was the visitor, Mr. Reid, short and stocky, who spoke with a heavy Scotch accent.

148

Mr. Brooks nodded, and the boys stood at attention in a row side by side. Then he waved in their direction and said with a smile, "These are the fastest messenger boys to be found anywhere, Mr. Reid."

"Umph!" Mr. Reid gave the boys a close hard look. "Are they good workers?"

Andy felt his cheeks turn red under Mr. Reid's look. Suddenly he thought how important Mr. Reid was in comparison with him, but he could be important to Mr. Reid. He should try to make Mr. Reid proud to have him working as a messenger boy. He stood straight and tall to make as good an impression as possible.

"Who's the wee tow-headed lad?" Mr. Reid asked abruptly.

"Andrew Carnegie—one of my best workers," replied Mr. Brooks.

"And where are you from, lad?" asked Mr. Reid turning to Andy.

"Dunfermline—I mean, Allegheny now, sir," Andy stammered.

Mr. Reid threw back his head and laughed. "Aye, a true Scot to name his homeland first. Why, I'm from Dunfermline, too!"

Before long Mr. Reid began to tell the boys stories about Scotland. Everyone had a good time visiting with him.

After Mr. Reid left, Andy said, "That surely was a surprise—to find that one of our big bosses came from Scotland. I think we passed inspection."

The other boys laughed. "Yes, I think we did, Andy," agreed George.

Later in the day Mr. Brooks called George and Andy into his office. "Boys, Mr. Reid likes all of you messengers and has arranged to get you some uniforms," he said. "The company will pay for the uniforms."

"Wow!" Andy cried. "Isn't that something?"

Mr. Brooks told George and Andy to tell the other boys. All were to go down to the nearby tailor shop and be measured for the uniforms as soon as they could.

Eagerly George and Andy told the other boys about the uniforms. The boys were measured and soon the new uniforms were ready.

Proudly Andy put on his new uniform at home. The jacket and knickerbockers were dark green, and the cap was made to match.

When Andy's brother Tom saw the handsome uniform he said, "Andy, you must be pretty important to have such fine clothes."

Andy laughed and rumpled Tom's blond hair. "Yes, I feel important dressed up like this, but I hope to be much more important later. Let's wait and see."

The following year passed happily for Andy. He enjoyed his work and the companionship of the other boys. After work he spent all the time he could reading. He borrowed books from his aunts and neighbors.

"I didn't have much schooling," he explained to Tom, "but I'm going to make up for it. I'm going to read all that I can."

In the fall of 1850 Aunt and Uncle Hogan moved away from Allegheny. They went to live in Ohio, where Uncle William lived. The Carnegies now had more money, so they moved into the larger house where the Hogans had lived. They were very happy here, except they greatly missed Uncle and Aunt Hogan.

Times were better for the Carnegies than they ever had been before. Every now and then Mrs. Carnegie slipped a shining coin into the old stocking in her drawer. This, she said, was a special savings—to pay back the money they had borrowed from Ailie Fargie to come to America. It was a great day when Andy helped his mother count the stocking full of money.

"One hundred dollars!" Andy cried as he put the last coin in the stocking.

Mrs. Carnegie smiled. "Yes, Andy, exactly enough to pay off our debt to Ailie Fargie." Soon the money was speeding on its way to Scotland, and for the first time since the Carnegies came to America they were out of debt.

Andy soon discovered another new world— the world of the theater. Frequently there were telegrams to be delivered to the actors or actresses at the Pittsburgh Theater.

One evening Andy hurried to the theater with the last telegram he had to deliver before he went home for the night. He entered the theater by the stage door and delivered the telegram to the manager back-stage.

As Andy turned to leave, he was surprised to hear an actor's voice coming from on stage. He drew close to the wing at the sides of the stage and peeked through. There in the center of the

stage a short distance away, he saw an actor rehearsing his lines. He listened closely and heard the actor's words flow out through the great empty theater. They sounded very much like somebody reciting beautiful poetry.

For sometime Andy watched, spell-bound. "I've never heard anything like this before," he whispered. "It's wonderful!"

"Yes," the manager answered softly at his side. "That's James Murdoch, one of the most famous actors in America. He's preparing to do 'Hamlet' here tonight."

"Now I know," Andy said eagerly. " 'Hamlet' was written by William Shakespeare. My Uncle Lauder told me about his great plays, but I've never seen one acted out before."

Later Andy looked out beyond the stage at the empty theater. It was one of the biggest in the United States, the manager said.

The theater seemed like a grand place to Andy.

The boxes were rose-colored and the seats were crimson, edged with velvet and fastened down with brass tacks. The draperies were gold embroidered, and crystal chandeliers hung from the ceiling. At the back of the theater was the balcony, and above the balcony was the gallery. Many poor people sat in the gallery because the seats were cheaper.

"I certainly would like to see a play," Andy said with enthusiasm.

"Well, the next time you bring us a telegram, come close to curtain time. Then I'll try to find a free seat for you."

"Thanks!" said Andy with happy surprise. "I'll be back soon." He thanked the manager again and hurried home as fast as he could to tell Tom of his good fortune.

After this Andy spent many evenings at the theater. He soon knew some of the lines of Shakespeare's plays by heart. He saw some of the same plays over and over again, and yet he never grew tired of them.

Before long Andy came to know the names of some of the most famous actors and actresses in America. Whenever any of them came to Pittsburgh, he never missed a chance to see them. Clad in his green messenger's uniform, he became a familiar figure to the stage hands and the manager.

Whenever a telegram had to be delivered to the theater, Andy made sure that he could deliver it. The other messenger boys were more anxious to deliver telegrams outside the city limits. For each one of these the messenger got an extra ten cents.

Three boys in the office—Harry, Davy, and Bob—disagreed with one another about their earnings. One day Andy found the three boys having an argument on the street. "You've received more than your share this week," said

Harry, shaking his fists angrily at Davy and stepping forward threateningly.

"What are you talking about?" shouted Bob. "You both have received more than I this week. I'm the one underpaid."

Andy was surprised and startled. All these boys were his friends, and he could scarcely believe they were quarreling. Quickly he shouted, "Wait, boys, wait. What's the matter?"

Davy answered, "Harry and Bob get all the out-of-town wires. Now I want my share of these wires to earn the extra ten cents."

"Just a minute," argued Bob. "First come, first served. I started to work here before you did, so the wires are rightly mine."

"That's no argument," cried Harry putting up his fists, ready to fight.

"Hold everything," interrupted Andy. "We're supposed to be good friends, and we won't get anywhere, fighting over bonus telegrams."

158

"Have you a better idea, Andy?" asked Davy, giving Harry and Bob a hard look. "All I want is a fair share."

"That's all I want, too," put in Bob.

"How about you, Harry?" asked Andy.

"The same with me," replied Harry. "I guess I have made more extra money this week than anybody else, but I haven't cheated. I've just been watching for those telegrams."

"What's your idea, Andy?" Davy asked.

Just then George joined the group. He said nothing but paused to listen.

"Well, if George agrees, we all could deliver the out-of-town wires as they come in—whoever is free at the time to deliver them. Then at the end of the week we could divide all the bonus money equally."

Harry looked puzzled. "You mean we could put the ten cents in a jar or something? Then at the end of the week we could divide it?"

"Yes, that's my suggestion, Harry," said Andy. "Then each will do a fair share of delivering the telegrams, and each will get an equal share of the bonus money."

The boys thought briefly about Andy's idea and agreed that it sounded like a fair arrangement. "It will save a lot of hard feelings and maybe a fight or two," said George good-naturedly. He turned to Andy. "You act as treasurer, Andy. Keep the extra money and divide it up at the end of each week."

Davy, Harry, and Bob were glad to settle their dispute in this manner. They apologized to one another for getting angry and went back to work with smiles on their faces.

Andy Becomes an Operator

ANDY was happy to find during the following weeks that his bonus plan was successful. The boys had no further arguments with one another, and at the end of each week, they shared equally in the bonus.

Andy always was eager for a workday to begin and arrived at the office early. Often he was the only one there, because the telegraph operator hadn't yet come to work. In order to pass the time, he taught himself the telegraph code. This code was the system of dots and dashes which operators used to send messages over the telegraph lines.

Occasionally the telegraph operator was late to work. Whenever this happened, Andy tried to see whether he could understand the clicking on the machine. The constant clicking confused him at first, but soon he was able to make out letters and words. The more he listened, the more he could understand.

One morning when the operator was late getting to work, Andy heard a message being repeated on the machine. He listened closely and discovered that the message was urgent. The sender seemed to be frantic.

"Can anyone take this message? Can anyone take this message?" came the call.

Andy longed to answer. He felt sure that he could take the message, if it came in slowly. "I must try!" he decided. "Since the message is urgent, someone should take it so that it can be delivered. I'll take it down by hand from the sounds and then deliver it."

Hastily he seated himself at the operator's desk. He switched on the sending key and replied to Philadelphia: "Send your message and repeat it slowly. I can take it. Carnegie."

There was a pause after he finished, but soon the machine began to click out a message. He hadn't learned how to operate the receiving instrument, but hoped to be able to translate the sounds, if they came in slowly enough. Quickly he wrote down the letters on a pad, as he listened to the sounds.

Andy looked at his writing and was able to make out most of the message. Then the sender repeated the message and Andy was able to fill in all the gaps.

He rushed from the office to deliver the telegram. When he returned he told Mr. Brooks what he had done. "I know I shouldn't have taken the message, but it was so urgent I didn't know what else to do," he said.

Andy was afraid Mr. Brooks might be angry, but Mr. Brooks' answer surprised him. "I'm proud of you, Andy," he said. "Someday we'll need another telegraph operator, and when the time comes, I'll give you the job."

Andy had never been happier in his life and could hardly wait to tell his family. He continued to learn all that he could about the machine and the code, and in 1851, he was given a job as an operator. By now he had learned so much about the work that he could send and receive messages very rapidly.

Andy taught himself to take incoming messages by ear. This meant that he didn't need the cumbersome receiving instrument or the copyist to translate the messages into words. He translated sounds into letters and words.

The news of Andy's trick traveled rapidly through the city. There were only two other men in the country who could take messages by

ear. In time Andy was sent to other offices to help with telegraph work.

One night Andy wrote of his experiences to his cousin Dod in Scotland. "I have been away from home for the past two weeks," he wrote. "I was at Greensburg, a small town about thirty miles from Pittsburgh taking charge of the telegraph office. I have quit delivering messages now and have become an operator."

In the years that followed Andy continued to write to his cousin Dod. He wrote not only news about the family but also about this great, fast-growing country in America.

When Andy was seventeen years of age, he started to night school. He was interested in business, and he felt that he should learn book-keeping. He was a good student and wanted to learn as much as he could while he was young. Always he watched for an opportunity to learn.

One day Andy's friend Harry came with some

surprising news. "Andy, have you ever heard of Colonel Anderson?" he asked.

"Of course," Andy answered. "He's a retired manufacturer who has made a fortune and lives in Allegheny."

"Well, we're lucky to have him," Harry went on. "I took a telegram to him today and he showed me the big library in his home. He said that any of us working boys can borrow his books free of charge. We can come to his house to get books any Saturday morning and return them the following Saturday morning."

Andy was amazed. Nowhere in the country was there a library where persons could borrow books without paying rental charges.

"This is a chance of a lifetime!" he cried excitedly. "Why, the Colonel must have books on just about everything! I'll be the first one at his house next Saturday morning."

"Oh, no," said Harry. "I'll be first."

Andy became a regular borrower of Colonel Anderson's books. He read all of Shakespeare's plays and all the American history books he could find. Then he read essays, biographies, and histories of other countries.

"Colonel Anderson is anxious to help us boys who work," Andy told his mother. "He says that reading and learning are the most important things we can do in our spare time. He says that we can get a good education from his books, even though we can't go to school."

"He's right, Andy," said Mrs. Carnegie. "If you keep on reading, you'll become an educated man—a self-educated man."

A faraway look came into Andy's eyes. "Wouldn't it be wonderful," he said, "if there were libraries everywhere like the Colonel's, where people could borrow books free?"

"Maybe such a dream can come true some-day, Andy," Mrs. Carnegie answered.

Andy Works for
the Railroad

In 1852 there was a great celebration in Pittsburgh. The Pennsylvania Railroad was completed, and the city of Pittsburgh was now more important than ever. It was linked by railroad with the East and with the West.

Coal and iron now could be shipped faster and more conveniently by railroad than by riverboat. Also people could travel faster than they could by riverboat or stagecoach.

The following year Thomas A. Scott, superintendent of the Pennsylvania Railroad in Pittsburgh, offered seventeen-year-old Andy a job. "The Pennsylvania Railroad is a great pioneering railroad," he said, "and here is a chance to get in on the ground floor. I should like you to join us as a clerk and telegraph operator. How do you feel about coming?"

Andy liked Mr. Scott and knew that a job with the railroad would offer him a great opportunity for advancement. If he worked hard, he would not have to wait long for a promotion and a bigger salary. His starting salary would be thirty-five dollars a month.

Andy accepted the job eagerly. "I'll be happy to accept the position and will work hard for you," he said.

Andy found the work in the new office exciting. He tried to be as helpful to Mr. Scott as he could. He learned the numbers of all the trains, what they carried, and where they were going. He knew the names of the men who were operating the trains. He helped to see that all the men reported to work when they were needed.

Some of the men who worked on the railroad were hard to manage. They had worked on riverboats before the railroad was opened and had become very independent. Often they argued with Andy, but he didn't let them frighten him. Soon they came to like him and were glad to do whatever he asked of them.

In 1855 Andy's father died and the family was very sad. "I'll do my best," Andy said to himself, "to give my mother and brother a good home. Fortunately I have a good job. This is only the beginning. I'm determined to work my way to the top!"

One day shortly after his father's death Andy came home excited. "Mother!" he exclaimed, eager to tell of his new opportunity. "Mr. Scott says that he can help me make a lot of money—besides what I earn at my job."

His mother smiled. "How, Andy?" she asked. "How can you make money besides working?"

"By purchasing ten shares of Adams Express Company stock, but I'll need to borrow five hundred dollars," Andy explained hurriedly. "A share of stock is an investment—it's like buying part of the company."

Mrs. Carnegie nodded for him to go on. "If I own part of the Adams Express Company, I'll share in its profits. Mr. Scott says the company is growing rapidly and is certain to make more and more money."

"How much will you earn from the investment," asked Mrs. Carnegie thoughtfully.

"At least fifty cents a share each month and maybe more," Andy cried. "If I own ten shares, I'll get five dollars a month."

Mrs. Carnegie's eyes glistened. "Tell Mr. Scott that you'll get the money."

Andy shouted with joy and gave his mother a big hug. At once Mrs. Carnegie wrote to her brother, William Morrison, who lived in Ohio,

172

and arranged to borrow the money. Then Andy took the money to Mr. Scott and within a few days became the proud owner of ten shares of stock in the company.

A few months later he found a white envelope on his desk, addressed to "Andrew Carnegie, Esquire." At one corner of the envelope was the round stamp of the Adams Express Company.

Andy held his breath as he slit open the envelope. It held only one long slip of paper, a check for ten dollars.

That evening, Andy, Tom, and their mother gathered about the kitchen table. Andy showed Tom and his mother the check. They could hardly believe their eyes.

Mrs. Carnegie smiled. "This is a new way of earning money, Andy," she said. "You've earned it without doing any work."

Andy laughed. "Yes, it's the money that's working. This is just the beginning, Mother. I'll see that Uncle William is paid back as soon as possible for helping us."

In 1856 Mr. Scott became general superintendent of the Pennsylvania Railroad and moved to Altoona, Pennsylvania. He promoted Andy to be his private secretary and raised his salary to fifty dollars a month.

The Carnegies sold their house in Allegheny and moved to a much larger house in Altoona. Young Carnegie's fortunes were growing.

Soon after Carnegie moved to Altoona, he made a business trip to Ohio. He sat in the last seat of the rear car, listening to the rhythmic click of the coach wheels and looking at the changing scenery along the way.

Suddenly a stranger spoke to him. "Mr. Carnegie, the conductor told me you are connected with the railroad."

"That's right," young Carnegie said, puzzled.

"My name is T. T. Woodruff," said the

stranger. "I would like to talk with you about an important business venture."

Carnegie grinned. "I'm always interested in business, Mr. Woodruff. Please sit down."

In one hand Mr. Woodruff carried a small green bag. He placed the bag on his knees, opened it carefully, and lifted out a small model of a railroad car. "This," he said, "is a model of a railroad car I've invented. The car is designed for night traveling—a sleeping car."

Carnegie was amazed by what he saw. Quickly he realized what a revolutionary invention this was. If passengers could sleep in comfort on a train, he realized, many more people would be willing to travel at night. What a growth in business this could mean!

When Carnegie returned to Altoona, he told Mr. Scott about Woodruff's idea. Soon new sleeping cars were put into operation and became a great success. Then Carnegie bought an interest in the company that manufactured the cars and made a large sum of money.

In 1859 the Carnegies moved back to Pittsburgh. Mr. Scott had been made vice president of the railroad, and Carnegie became superintendent of the Pittsburgh division.

Carnegie's mother smiled with pride when he told her about his promotion. "Andy, you are only twenty-four, yet you have one of the finest jobs there are with the railroad. Now if you would get rid of that silly little beard, I'd be proud of you indeed!"

Carnegie laughed and ran his hand over the thin beard round his chin. "Oh, no, Mother!" he said. "This beard makes me look older!"

At twenty-four Carnegie looked more like a boy than a man. He was determined, however, to show the business world that he was a man— and a man of action, at that!

One of the first things Carnegie did as super-

intendent was make sixteen-year-old Tom his clerk. Next he made his old friend David Mc-Cargo superintendent of the telegraph office.

In 1861, during the War between the States, Mr. Scott became Assistant Secretary of War in charge of transportation. At once he invited Carnegie to come to Washington to help him. They worked day and night to organize a force of train repairmen and telegraphers.

One day in Alexandria, Virginia, Carnegie helped to load wounded men onto a hospital train. He was horrified and said bitterly, "I hate war! Someday—somehow—I'm going to do everything possible to prevent wars."

For eight months Carnegie worked with Mr. Scott in Washington. At last their job was done and they returned to Pennsylvania.

Carnegie worked hard for the railroad, but he found his interests gradually broadening. He invested money in a variety of business projects.

One was an iron mill, and another was the oil industry. Soon he found these other interests were occupying most of his time.

"I can't do both—work for the railroad and work for myself, too," he decided one day. So in 1865 he resigned his job with the railroad. He was in his thirtieth year, and now he was in business for himself!

At this young age Andrew Carnegie set out to mould a new career in life.

The Nation Builder

FROM 1861 to 1865 Andrew Carnegie observed the terrible things that war can do to a country and its people. He was happy when peace came and the States were united again. Immediately he realized that much building and rebuilding would need to be done.

Now that the war was over, Carnegie could foresee a great period of prosperity and growth. Both men and money would be free to carry on westward expansion in the country.

There was the wealth of a continent to develop. The plains and the fertile valleys of the West offered hard-working people a great opportunity. Soon the wandering Indian tribes and huge herds of buffalo would have to give way to thousands and thousands of settlers.

Carnegie realized that many men who had fought in the war would want to go West to seek their fortunes. They would go to farm rich new land or to start new businesses. Railroads would become more and more important as a means of transportation. Horses and wagons, oxcarts, steamboats, and canal boats would be too slow for transportation in the years ahead.

Even during the war Carnegie had seen this growth of the West coming. There had been a great demand for new iron rails, which wore out rapidly and had to be replaced. New roadbeds had to be constructed and new bridges had to be built. Most of the bridges were made of wood and were easily destroyed by wind or by fire.

Carnegie became interested in building iron bridges to replace wooden bridges. "Iron bridges," he said, "would be safe and strong. They would help to prevent long delays in rail traffic. They would be good for the railroads and good for the country."

Soon Carnegie became a partner in the Keystone Bridge Company. This was the first company to build iron bridges in America.

In the next few years Carnegie became interested in several other business projects. In 1866 he helped to form the Pittsburgh Locomotive Works. Then he and his brother Tom founded the Union Iron Mills to provide the iron needed for building bridges. He helped to form another company to make iron rails.

These were prosperous years for Carnegie. By now he was connected with a half dozen different companies in America. In 1867 he and his mother left Pittsburgh and moved to New York. The sign on his new office door in New York read: "A. Carnegie: Investments."

Six years later Carnegie decided to manufacture steel. "The iron age has past," he explained to his mother. "Steel has become king!"

Mrs. Carnegie looked puzzled. "My old friends don't agree with me," Carnegie went on, "but I'll show them. Before long railroads will replace all their iron rails with steel rails. Iron rails have to be replaced every six weeks or so, especially on curves, but steel rails will last for long periods of time."

Up to now nearly all the steel in the world had been manufactured in England. Recently a man named Henry Bessemer of England had developed a new process of producing steel better and more cheaply.

Carnegie had visited England and watched steel being made by the Bessemer process. When he returned, he was determined to make steel in the same manner in America.

In 1873 Carnegie helped to organize a new

steel company to be known as the Edgar Thompson Works, located at Braddock, Pennsylvania. He hired one of the best men he could find to run the plant, a man with wide experience in the steel industry.

By now there was a fast-growing market for steel—rails for railroads, machinery for factories, machinery for farms. Soon the Edgar Thompson Works began to excel all its competitors in the output of steel. By 1880 it was making one-seventh of all the Bessemer steel produced in the United States. In 1881 Carnegie combined all his business interests related to the manufacture of steel in one company known as Carnegie Brothers and Company.

Through the years Carnegie had led a very strenuous life. He felt that he needed a vacation, so he invited a few friends to go with him and his mother on a trip through England and Scotland. It took the travelers six weeks to make the trip, but it was a happy party and there was no need for them to hurry.

When Carnegie and his party reached Dunfermline, they were met by Uncle Lauder. All the people of the town turned out to give him a friendly welcome. Then he gave the town a public library—the first of several thousand libraries which he was able to establish.

When Carnegie returned to the United States, he decided to spend less time working. He especially wanted time to make life as comfortable as possible for his aging mother. In 1886, however, both his mother and brother Tom died, and he was the only one left in the family.

One year later Carnegie married Louise Whitfield, whom he had known for many years. She was a capable horse woman, and he had enjoyed riding horses with her. Following their marriage they spent their honeymoon in Scotland, where Carnegie saw many old friends again.

As the years passed, Carnegie and his wife spent more and more time in Scotland. He knew that the men who worked for him were good managers. They could be trusted to run his enterprises skillfully. Besides, he was quick to take advantage of any new business talent he found.

In time Carnegie became interested in a young man named Henry Clay Frick, who was an important producer of coke. Carnegie needed coke badly for the manufacture of steel.

"We must get this man to join us," Carnegie told his associates. "He is ambitious and able and he can supply us with the vast quantities of coke that we need. He would help to make our company even greater."

Carnegie's associates were quick to realize the importance of his idea. If Frick would join them, the greatest coke producer would be united with the greatest steel producer. Frick was asked to join Carnegie's company. He agreed, and within a short period of time became the executive head of the steel company.

In the summer of 1892, when Carnegie and his wife were in Scotland, trouble came to the Carnegie plant in Homestead, Pennsylvania. Some of the workers had organized a union and demanded a greater share in the company's profits. Frick felt that their demands were unreasonable and announced that he would employ non-union men to take their places. He thought that in this way he could keep the plant going. Few workers belonged to the union.

Soon the trouble grew worse, and the union men threatened to prevent new workers from entering the plant. The company hired armed detectives to keep the plant open. When the detectives arrived on a barge, they exchanged shots with the union men watching at the plant.

The conflict got out of hand and the governor of Pennsylvania sent the state militia to restore order. Three detectives had been wounded and five steel workers had been killed.

When Carnegie heard of the trouble, he was greatly disturbed. "Frick should have found a better way of handling the strike. There must have been some way of settling it peacefully, before persons were wounded and killed. Possibly if he had been on the job, there wouldn't have been a strike to begin with."

From this time on Carnegie and Frick were less friendly than before. Finally, after many disagreements, Frick resigned.

In 1897 a daughter was born to Mr. and Mrs. Carnegie. Shortly after her birth Carnegie bought an estate in Scotland, called Skibo Castle. There the family spent many happy holidays.

As the years passed, Carnegie began to think of retiring. He had accumulated a huge fortune, and was satisfied with his achievements. Now he was eager to turn his attention to other people.

Somehow he hoped that he could help other people with some of his money.

In 1901 J. Pierpont Morgan, the most important banker in the United States, offered to buy the Carnegie Steel Company. Carnegie considered the offer and named his price—four hundred million dollars. Morgan agreed and reorganized the Carnegie Steel Company into the United States Steel Corporation.

Now Carnegie was free to concentrate on distributing his wealth to help other people in the world. His first gift was to his former workers. He set aside four million dollars for the Andrew Carnegie Relief Fund, to be used for pensions and compensations for accidents.

Next he turned to establishing free public libraries. He appreciated the importance of books and their relation to learning. He remembered how he had turned to books to make up for his limited schooling. Now he wanted to provide books for others who were eager to learn. The best way to do this, he felt, was to establish free libraries. Accordingly, he gave a large sum to the New York City Public Library and built 2,811 free public libraries throughout the English-speaking world.

In other directions, Carnegie established the Carnegie Institute in Washington, D. C., for scientific research. He founded the Carnegie Institute of Technology in Pittsburgh, to provide technical training for students. He provided the Carnegie Foundation in New York for the advancement of teaching.

Carnegie also made generous contributions to Scotch, British, and Irish universities. In Dunfermline he built a school for technical and manual training, a concert hall, a social center, and an athletic field. In addition he provided a public park, which all members of Dunfermline could use for recreation and enjoyment.

In later life Carnegie became interested in promoting international peace. To advance the cause of peace, he built the famous Peace Palace at the Hague, in the Netherlands. At the same time he created the Carnegie Endowment for International Peace.

In 1911 Carnegie established the Carnegie Corporation to continue his distribution of money for worthy causes. Then, even after his death, his money could be used for the benefit of mankind. He kept only a small percentage of his wealth for himself and his family.

In 1919 Andrew Carnegie died at his estate in the Berkshire hills of Massachusetts. Through his achievements and philanthropy, he had improved the lives of millions of people.

As Elihu Root, a noted lawyer and statesman, said, "he belonged to that great race of nation builders who have made the development of America the wonder of the world."

More About This Book

WHEN ANDREW CARNEGIE LIVED

1835   ANDREW CARNEGIE WAS BORN IN DUNFERM-
LINE, SCOTLAND, NOVEMBER 25.

There were twenty-four states in the Union.

William IV was King of Great Britain.

Andrew Jackson was President.

The population of the United States was about
14,960,000.

1835–   ANDY LIVED IN DUNFERMLINE AND AFTER 1848
1853   IN ALLEGHENY, PENNSYLVANIA.

Samuel Morse invented the telegraph, 1835.

The United States acquired the Oregon Terri-
tory north of California, 1846.

The Mexican War was fought, 1846–48.

The Mormons reached Great Salt Lake, 1847.

Gold was discovered in California, 1848.

Mail was first delivered overland to the west
coast, 1850.

Harriet Beecher Stowe's *Uncle Tom's Cabin*
was published, 1852.

1853–1865	YOUNG CARNEGIE ACHIEVED SUCCESS WORKING FOR THE PENNSYLVANIA RAILROAD.

The first railroad was completed, connecting the East and Middle West, 1853.

The War between the States was fought, 1861–1865.

The first Pullman railroad sleeping car was built, 1864.

1865–1901	CARNEGIE LEFT THE PENNSYLVANIA RAILROAD TO ENTER THE IRON AND STEEL BUSINESS.

The first transcontinental railroad was completed, 1869.

Thomas Edison invented the phonograph, 1878, and the electric light bulb, 1879.

Henry Ford built his first automobile, 1896.

1901–1919	CARNEGIE RETIRED TO DEVOTE HIS TIME TO PHILANTHROPIC WORKS.

Wilbur and Orville Wright flew the first heavier-than-air aircraft, 1903.

The Panama Canal was completed and opened to world traffic, 1914.

World War I was fought, 1914–1918.

194

1919 ANDREW CARNEGIE DIED IN LENOX, MASSA-
CHUSETTS, AUGUST 11.

There were forty-eight states in the Union.

Woodrow Wilson was President.

The population of the country was about 128,070,000.

DO YOU REMEMBER?

1. Where did Andy Carnegie and his family live when he was a boy?

2. How did Andy make a boy angry when he went to get water from the village well?

3. What story about his troubles did Andy tell his parents around the fireside?

4. Why did the workers in Scotland riot on the streets and threaten factory owners?

5. How did Uncle Lauder encourage Dod and Andy to memorize poems and plays?

6. How did Andy secure a pair of rabbits to go in the rabbit business?

7. How did Andy get boys to agree to gather feed for his rabbits?

8. How did machines in factories cause workers on hand looms to lose their jobs?

9. Why did the Carnegie family finally decide to move to America?

10. What different jobs did Andy hold soon after the family settled in Allegheny?

11. How did young Carnegie get promoted from messenger boy to telegraph operator?

12. How did Carnegie achieve success working for the Pennsylvania Railroad?

13. How did Carnegie amass a fortune in the iron and steel industry?

14. How did Carnegie give away most of his fortune for the welfare of others?

IT'S FUN TO LOOK UP THESE THINGS

1. Why has weaving long been an important industry in Scotland?

2. What was the Industrial Revolution that caused hand weavers to lose their jobs?

3. How have railroads played an important part in the growth of the United States?

4. Who invented the telegraph and what was the first telegraphic message?

5. Why has Pittsburgh become one of the most important iron and steel centers in the world?

6. What is the famous Bessemer process which Carnegie used to manufacture steel?

INTERESTING THINGS YOU CAN DO

1. Collect pictures of men wearing Scottish kilts for a display on the bulletin board.

2. Make a list of the leading kinds of materials weavers use in making cloth.

3. Explain what is meant by the Morse code which is used in sending telegrams.

4. Prepare a short article telling how steel is made to read to your class.

5. Draw a map showing where Pittsburgh is located at the head of the Ohio River.

6. Visit a library which Carnegie built and report what you find to your classmates.

7. Make a list of the organizations which Carnegie founded or to which he gave money.

OTHER BOOKS YOU MAY ENJOY READING

Andrew Carnegie and the Age of Steel, Katherine B. Shippen. Random House.

George Pullman: Young Sleeping Car Builder, Elisabeth P. Myers. Trade and School Editions, Bobbs-Merrill.

Iron and Steel, Pennsylvania Writers' Project. Whitman.

Let's Go to a Steel Mill, Erma Green. Putnam.

Men on Iron Horses, Edith McCall. Childrens Press.

Story of Scotland, Lawrence Stenhouse. Watts.

INTERESTING WORDS IN THIS BOOK

Abbey (ăb′ĭ) : monastery or convent where religious persons lived and prayed

bagpipe (băg′pīp′) : wind musical instrument, including a leather bag, flutelike tube, and three or four sound pipes

Bannockburn (băn′ŭk bûrn′) : town in Scotland, where a famous battle was fought in 1314

Bessemer process (bĕs′ĕ mẽr prŏs′ĕs) : process of changing iron to steel by forcing air through the molten iron

198

bobbin (bŏb'ĭn) : spool or reel around which yarn or thread is wound for weaving

chandeliers (shăn'dĕ lērz') : light fixtures with branches that hang from the ceiling

cobblestones (kŏb''l stōnz) : rounded stones once used for paving streets

coke (kōk) : fuel made from coal

corn laws (kôrn' lôz') : English laws that controlled the sale of grains such as wheat

cumbersome (kŭm'bĕr sŭm) : clumsy

douse (douz) : drench

fortune (fôr'tŭn) : success in life, often measured in wealth

gangplank (găng' plăngk') : movable platform used for boarding or leaving a ship

kilt (kĭlt) : skirtlike costume worn on special occasions by men and boys in Scotland

knickerbockers (nĭk'ĕr bŏk'ĕrz) : knee-length pants once widely worn by boys

militia (mĭ lĭsh'à) : group of citizens organized as a military unit but called into service only for emergency purposes

199

moor (mŏŏr) : open wasteland usually covered with heather

percentage (pẽr sĕnt′ĭj) : part of a whole

permission (pẽr mĭsh′ŭn) : consent

ramshackle (răm′shăk′′l) : rundown, appearing ready to collapse

rehearsing (rė hûrs′ĭng) : practicing in preparation for a real performance

revolutionary (rĕv′ȯ lū′shŭn ĕr′ĭ) : radical

rhythmic (rĭth′mĭk) : moving regularly

riot (rī′ŭt) : wild public disturbance

routine (rōō tēn′) : regular way of doing things

satchel (sach′′l) : small bag

shuttles (shŭt′′lz) : instruments used to pass thread back and forth across a loom in weaving

temporarily (tĕm′pȯ răr′ĭ lĭ) : momentarily

tide (tīd) : rising and falling of the ocean

toddle (tŏd′′l) : walk with short, tottering steps

tow-headed (tō′ hĕd′ĕd) : having very light blond hair

urgent (ûr′jĕnt) : needing immediate attention

Childhood

OF FAMOUS AMERICANS

COLONIAL DAYS

JAMES OGLETHORPE, *Parks*
JOHN ALDEN, *Burt*
MYLES STANDISH, *Stevenson*
PETER STUYVESANT, *Widdemer*
POCAHONTAS, *Seymour*
PONTIAC, *Peckham*
SQUANTO, *Stevenson*
VIRGINIA DARE, *Stevenson*
WILLIAM BRADFORD, *Smith*
WILLIAM PENN, *Mason*

STRUGGLE for INDEPENDENCE

ANTHONY WAYNE, *Stevenson*
BEN FRANKLIN, *Stevenson*
BETSY ROSS, *Weil*
CRISPUS ATTUCKS, *Millender*
DAN MORGAN, *Bryant*
ETHAN ALLEN, *Winders*
FRANCIS MARION, *Steele*
GEORGE ROGERS CLARK, *Wilkie*
GEORGE WASHINGTON, *Stevenson*
ISRAEL PUTNAM, *Stevenson*
JOHN HANCOCK, *Cleven*
JOHN PAUL JONES, *Snow*
MARTHA WASHINGTON, *Wagoner*
MOLLY PITCHER, *Stevenson*
NATHAN HALE, *Stevenson*
NATHANAEL GREENE, *Peckham*
PATRICK HENRY, *Barton*
PAUL REVERE, *Stevenson*
TOM JEFFERSON, *Monsell*

EARLY NATIONAL GROWTH

ABIGAIL ADAMS, *Wagoner*
ALEC HAMILTON, *Higgins*
ANDY JACKSON, *Stevenson*
DAN WEBSTER, *Smith*
DEWITT CLINTON, *Widdemer*
DOLLY MADISON, *Monsell*
ELI WHITNEY, *Snow*
ELIAS HOWE, *Corcoran*
FRANCIS SCOTT KEY, *Stevenson*
HENRY CLAY, *Monsell*
JAMES FENIMORE COOPER, *Winders*
JAMES MONROE, *Widdemer*
JOHN AUDUBON, *Mason*
JOHN JACOB ASTOR, *Anderson*
JOHN MARSHALL, *Monsell*
JOHN QUINCY ADAMS, *Weil*
LUCRETIA MOTT, *Burnett*
MATTHEW CALBRAITH PERRY, *Scharbach*
NANCY HANKS, *Stevenson*
NOAH WEBSTER, *Higgins*
OLIVER HAZARD PERRY, *Long*
OSCEOLA, *Clark*
RACHEL JACKSON, *Govan*
ROBERT FULTON, *Henry*
SAMUEL MORSE, *Snow*
SEQUOYAH, *Snow*
STEPHEN DECATUR, *Smith*
STEPHEN FOSTER, *Higgins*
WASHINGTON IRVING, *Widdemer*
ZACK TAYLOR, *Wilkie*

WESTWARD MOVEMENT

BRIGHAM YOUNG, *Jordan and Frisbee*
BUFFALO BILL, *Stevenson*
DANIEL BOONE, *Stevenson*
DAVY CROCKETT, *Parks*
GAIL BORDEN, *Paradis*
JED SMITH, *Burt*
JESSIE FREMONT, *Wagoner*
JIM BOWIE, *Winders*
JIM BRIDGER, *Winders*
KIT CARSON, *Stevenson*